Practical Engineering Drawing

Practical Engineering Drawing

Brian Hadley

Addison Wesley Longman Limited
Edinburgh Gate, Harlow
Essex CM20 2JE, England
and Associated Companies throughout the world

© Addison Wesley Longman Limited 1999

First published 1999

British Library Cataloguing in Publication Data
A catalogue entry for this title is available from the British Library

ISBN 0-582-36983-5

Set by 32 in Garamond 10/12 and Univers
Produced by Addison Wesley Longman Singapore (Pte)
Printed in Singapore

Contents

Preface

This book is aimed at the student studying the Engineering Advanced GNVQ Additional Unit 'Engineering Drawing'. It is structured such that students with little or no experience of Engineering Drawing as well as those with considerably more may, by using this book, progress through the topic areas at their own pace gaining knowledge of the subject and understanding how to apply this to achieve success in the unit.

Many Engineering Advanced GNVQ course teams plan the course such that the unit Design Development is in the latter half of the course as this unit requires the application of knowledge gained in units such as Mathematics and Mechanical and Electrical Science, as well as Engineering Drawing. This book together with notes and completed assignments will also act as a study aide when working on the unit 'Design Development'.

Each chapter is structured such that students may work at their own pace within the class environment, or on their own with tutorial help. To assist both lecturer and student a study plan and assessment plan have been included in the Assessment chapter thus giving a guide to the study requirements and the possible time requirements. In addition to the plans, a table is included indicating the units, elements, and performance criteria that will be achieved on successful completion of the work outlined in this book. This will also assist the student in the cross referencing required when compiling their portfolio.

As planning and the meeting of target dates are part of the GNVQ requirements this book will assist students in the preparation of planning sheets for all themes as well as enabling the student to set realistic target times.

Students and lecturers may find the material included in this book also applicable to the Manufacturing Advanced GNVQ where the course content has a requirement for Drawing and possibly Design.

In addition to those studying GNVQ students working towards the BTEC units Engineering Drawing (1675C) and Computer-Aided Drawing (1673C) may find it an appropriate aide to study.

Brian Hadley

Chapter 1

The activities of the drawing office

The purpose of this chapter is to give the student a knowledge of the workings of the traditional and computerised drawing office. The principal elements and operation of the drawing office are described so that students may enhance their knowledge and understanding of:

- The work carried out in the drawing office.
- Standards used and adhered to in the drawing office.
- Drawing office communications.
- The advantages and the problems of the computerisation of a drawing office.

The way in which a drawing office is organised and how this organisation fits into the structure of the company may have some effect on its activities. Figures 1.1 and 1.2 illustrate a possible structure of both a drawing office and a company. The diagram shown in Fig. 1.1(a) illustrates a drawing office from a fairly large engineering company with a number of **sections** each under the control of a section leader. The number of sections and the number of people shown in each section is only representative as this would vary considerably from company to company and according to the work being undertaken.

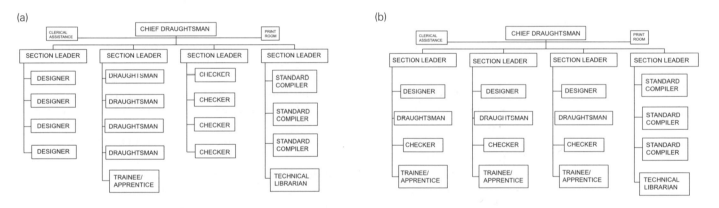

Fig. 1.1

The diagram shows one section dedicated to design work and all the necessary research and development required. Another section is dedicated to the preparation of detail drawings and a third to the checking of all aspects of a drawing. This requires the checking of aspects of the drawing such as the application of limits and fits, drawing standards and all calculations before receiving a signature of approval and being issued for use by the rest of the company. A fourth section is shown as having a number of areas, all supporting the drawing office. These areas are standards preparation and technical library provision. (As you understand more about the drawing office you will see the importance of this area of work.) Clerical assistance would also be required to help deal with the inevitable paperwork as will a print room to produce copies of the drawings and ensure the control and correct distribution of both new drawings and modified and re-issued drawings.

Some drawing offices are based on sections but with each section being responsible for a particular product range. The sections would therefore include its own designers, draughtsmen and checkers. There would still be a need for a separate section for standards and technical library support. This modified arrangement is shown in Fig. 1.1(b).

Fig. 1.2

Some large companies have a completely separate standards section or department. This section or department is used to produce the standards used by all the departments of the company from the drawing office to the methods of manufacture, purchase control and customer inquiry departments. This would be to help the company conform to the standards required by ISO 9000/BS 5750.

The work undertaken by those in the drawing office would vary considerably according to the experience and knowledge of each individual. Some designers/ draughtsmen may have worked considerably more in one area than other individuals and therefore this becomes their **area of expertise**.

Examples of this may be in such areas as casting and forging design, gearbox layout, switch design and layout, sheet metal work and many more areas that are found in engineering.

With many specialist areas some individuals may be the 'expert' in more than one area, particularly in the small drawing office. Those without areas of special interest, such as trainees and those who have only recently completed their training, will find that they will be working with a specialist. When that project is completed they may move on to work with another specialist thus gaining valuable experience and in time they may become a specialist.

Many people who enter a drawing office for the first time are often surprised to find that the whole day is not spent producing drawings. Some of the work undertaken by the drawing office may involve some or all of the following:

- Design production and development. This may involve many hours of research of various forms, many calculations and finish with what may appear to be an assembly drawing.
- Detail and assembly drawing production from the design and modified designs produced by the design staff.
- Compilation of parts lists for the drawings and assemblies.
- Compilation of an assembly schedule. A very necessary function of the drawing office. This will be used by subcontractors and customers as well as many different people throughout the company. All this adds information to the companies central database and aids such functions as ordering, assembly, repair and maintenance.
- Design and drawing modification. The modification may be necessary due to the development of manufacturing techniques, design upgrade or even due to error in the initial design.
- Parts list and assembly schedule modification. These must be up to date to ensure correct ordering, assembly, repair and maintenance etc.
- Document preparation for modified drawings and parts list to allow re-issue. A very necessary record of why the modification was implemented and what it entailed.
- Calculations of many types, e.g. determination of diameter and length of bolts, limits and fits under all operating conditions, gears and gear ratios and many others dependent on the work with which the company is involved.
- Research – particularly in design – into new ideas, alternative and new materials, alternative shapes, new methods of production and the effect on presentation and dimensioning of an item, what competitors are producing etc.

In addition to the above activities those involved in a drawing office may be required to have a knowledge or, at the very least, an understanding of the following topics.

Company standards

Many companies use their own standards based on British Standards and experience of the products and methods of production. These standards would be compiled and implemented after consultation by experienced engineers who will have direct contact with all parts of the company as well as suppliers and subcontractors.

Draughting standards

Drawings must conform to an acceptable and understandable standard to facilitate communication. The standards are usually based on British Standards and experience proven over a long period of time. These would be compiled by experienced engineering draughtsmen and only implemented after extensive consultation. This consultation would involve all areas from the initial design and drawing production through the selection of materials and on to final dispatch, including any legal requirements of the specific area of engineering in which the company is involved. Customer input to the development of the specification may have to be part of this.

Dimensioning standards

Usually based on British Standards and experience gained by the company over many years in its area of expertise. This would not only involve the drawing office but the manufacturing areas who have to apply and use these standards. The correct dimensioning and application of practical limits and fits and geometrical tolerances will provide interchangeability and help ensure a quality product is produced at a competitive price.

Material standards

This may include preferred materials and sizes with proven physical and chemical properties. These standards may be provided by material specialists together with consultation across the design, manufacturing, production and costing offices. This may enable a more limited range of material to be held in stock, thus helping to reduce overheads.

Standard parts

This is another means of controlling the amount of stock held in stores and ensuring that only parts which have been proven as suitable will be used. Examples common to many companies will be in the use of nuts, bolts and rivets etc. The control of nuts and bolts will also control the range of tools used to assemble the product, thus controlling the cost of production in more than one way.

Data sheets

Data sheets are produced by the company and/or specialist suppliers to determine optimum performance of an item. One example would be data sheets for roller and ball bearings which give all dimensions and tolerances and types of fit required as well as the working load and the range of working conditions.

Communications

This would include some of the following topics:

- **Drawing and contract numbering**
  This should involve a thorough knowledge of the system that ensures contract, design and detail drawings can be traced very quickly.
- **Coding of parts and assemblies**
  Again a knowledge of the logical system which allows complete traceability from the initial contract to despatch and, if necessary, to servicing and repair.
- **Drawing modification standards**
  A set of standards or rules that must be followed to ensure that all those involved from design to dispatch are working to the latest specification.
- **Planning for component manufacture**
  A knowledge of the methods of production available in the company and by approved subcontractors. Also the dimensioning and tolerancing required for both operation and manufacture of the product.
- **Quality control and inspection requirements**
  A good general knowledge of the requirements of quality control throughout the company and a more detailed knowledge of its effect on the production of the design and detail drawings.
- **Internal paper work**
  This area will vary from company to company, but it forms an essential part of the communication system and should be understood.

Many of these items may have a great deal of effect on the way drawings are initially issued and modified. These must be rigidly controlled to ensure all are working to the latest specification.

The computer in the drawing office

Many people today use the acronym CAD without considering its meaning. In this book we will use it to mean both computer-aided draughting (CAD) and computer-aided design and draughting (CADD).

So far in this chapter all we have considered is the traditional drawing office. As we consider the influence the computer has had on the drawing office it will be seen that the differences are not in the activities themselves but in the speed and accuracy at which results are achieved and how quickly they are communicated.

Figure 1.3 illustrates how CAD may be integrated within a computerised manufacturing system and how data generated by each area is made available to all other areas of the company. To those in the computerised drawing office CAD means a design and drawing process that uses the computers highly technical computer graphics system and computer software. This assists in the solution of the many mathematical problems associated with the design and will enhance design development techniques as well as influence many other areas associated with design and drawing production.

Before going into any detail as to what CAD can do it would be wise to keep in mind what it does not do. It is in fact similar to traditional design and draughting. Errors and omissions made by the designer and the draughtsperson will not be corrected by the computer. It may be much quicker for these errors and omissions to be corrected using a CAD system, but it does not replace the skill and knowledge of the designer. There is a saying which is worth repeating: 'Rubbish in, rubbish out'.

Rather than detail what CAD can do it would be more helpful to look at the advantages of CAD over the traditional system of design and drawing production. These are generally seen as:

- **Drawing production**
  It is generally agreed that a draughtsperson on a CAD system will produce drawings

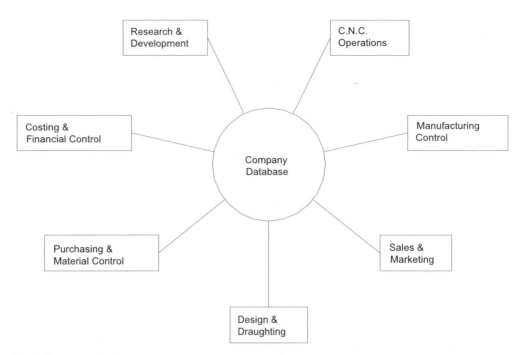

Fig. 1.3

at about three times the rate as that by conventional means, provided that the person has received the appropriate training. This is due in part to a number of automated features.

- **Drawing accuracy**

  The accuracy of a drawing can be increased greatly over the conventional method of drawing production. The pencil thickness and the draughtsperson's eye can lead to errors. With a CAD system a point on the monitor screen is an exact co-ordinate which can be selected with ease.

- **Drawing standards**

  All drawings from a company can look very similar. Items such as the line quality, printing and dimensioning can be controlled and standardised. Lines that have been removed will not leave an indentation and therefore a line, or mark, on the copies made. Construction lines can be 'hidden' thus enhancing the appearance of the drawing but remaining available for use at a latter stage of development.

- **Drawing and documentation repetition**

  On completion a drawing and its associated documentation can be stored and retrieved as and when required by all interested sections of the company. (*Note*: The system will not allow the drawing to be modified by just anyone.) CAD lends itself to the production of components of similar shape. In the production of tooling (e.g. jigs and fixtures) drawings do not have to be redrawn or traced and the shape created is accurate. The various shapes within each item, which have been accurately drawn by the draughtsperson, may be extracted from the computer file and used to generate the cutting tool path or press tool shape etc. A symbol library may be created and stored within the system, thus eliminating the repetitive task of drawing them. There is also a method of producing a **family of shapes**. Once a **master** has been produced the dimensions required will be entered as requested and a drawing produced. This advanced technique is called **parametrics**.

- **Additional techniques**

  There are a number techniques that are available to the CAD operator. One that will be used frequently is the Zoom facility. This allows the operator to magnify an area of the screen to the extent required and on completion return to the full drawing which should always be drawn full size. Others which aid drawing are Mirror, Hatch, Fillet, etc. (All these increase drawing speed and accuracy.)

  It should be noted that it is at the printing stage that the drawing is **scaled**. Although there may be views which are drawn at a suitable scale for clarity.

- **Analysis**
  The larger CAD systems will have additional facilities available and the small personal computer (PC) will probably allow the running of additional software in conjunction with the CAD software. These assist with the complex calculations required and perform them in a fraction of the time required by traditional means.

  One package that has made the transition from the large computer system to the PC is finite element analysis (FEA). This provides a means of producing calculations for the stress analysis of complex shapes.
- **Modelling techniques**
  Using the advantages created by the ability to calculate quickly and accurately the designer is able to produce more innovative shapes which can be quickly modified to enhance its use and manufacture thus saving time and money.
- **Design development**
  CAD can aid design and further reduce testing and development costs by simulation and reduce the need for the time and money spent on prototyping and model making.
- **Communications**
  Computers in the workplace will vastly improve the communications available if an integrated system is employed. This will allow all areas of the company to work closely with each other rather than in isolation.

So far all we have mentioned are the positive points about computerisation of the drawing office and other areas of the company. There is a negative side; this is usually seen as the **cost**. This is only one of a number of negative areas. In general these are seen as:

- Initial cost of hardware as compared to the cost of traditional drawing office equipment.
- The development of the database. This will require additional highly trained staff. A very necessary requirement if the system is to be used to its full potential.
- Support staff training. Again a very necessary requirement.
- Initial cost of purchasing the software, keeping it up to date.
- The training of the drawing staff in the use of computers and the CAD system.
- Time lost in transition from a conventional to a computerised system. This will also affect many of the associated areas within the company, e.g. manufacturing.
- Accommodation – a new situation may be required to house the computer system as well as the operators.
- Maintenance costs. Both hardware and software will need to be continually checked with upgrades being required at regular intervals.
- Consumables. (There always seems to be more paper where computers are used.)
- Training updates for both operators and support staff.
- Insurance costs.
- Downtime – computers do break down sometimes, particularly if the training and accommodation is not up to the required standards.
- The number of draughtspersons required may be less for the same output.
- Working practices will change; some staff may find it very difficult to adapt.
- Some staff may experience health problems. (There are Health and Safety Requirements that will have to be complied with, e.g. seating.)

Exercises

The following exercises require not only that the chapter be studied but that the student should endeavour to obtain additional information from other sources.

1 All detail drawings, assembly drawings and the necessary paperwork for a particular project have been completed. Explain briefly the next stage before the drawings are signed and released for use in the workshops

2 New ideas are continually required by a company to keep its products in demand. List five ways that these new ideas or modifications may be generated.

3 Make a list of ten different types of information that may be kept in a technical library.

4 Why is it necessary for 'standards' to be applied in an engineering company, why do they differ from company to company?

5 What is meant by **interchangeability**?

6 What are **data sheets** and how are they used in engineering?

7 When producing a drawing of a component or an assembly what advantages does a computer system give over the traditional system?

8 Explain briefly what the disadvantages are of a computerised drawing office.

9 Briefly explain how the use of a computer assists in the maintenance of company standards.

10 It is said that the use of a computer speeds up the design and development of a product to the production phase. Give five examples of how this is achieved.

Chapter 2

The equipment and instruments used in the traditional drawing office

The purpose of this chapter is to introduce the student to the equipment used in the traditional drawing office. This will enable the student to have a full appreciation of the application of:

- Some of the many forms of the traditional drawing board.
- The range of instruments used in the traditional drawing office.
- Some of the more popular drawing aids used.
- The costs involved.

The equipment used in the traditional drawing office is normally seen as:

- The drawing board – this has a number of forms and some will be illustrated.
- The drawing instruments. A range is illustrated but use is an individual choice.
- Measuring instruments. The work being undertaken will dictate selection.
- The set squares.
- The range of pencils and erasers available.
- Instruments to aid the drawing of curves. Selection and use is dependent on the work being undertaken and the skill of the draughtsperson.

Drawing board

This has many forms but in its simplest form it may just consist of a flat board of a size to suit the range of paper sizes (A0 to A3). The board material may be wood, plastic or plastic-coated wood. The underside may have battens in some form to aid rigidity and ensure it stays flat. The working edge of the wooden board (usually the left-hand vertical edge) may have a dark ebony strip giving a hard longer life to the edge. The plastic boards up to A3 size usually have a set of grooves around all sides to act as the location for the slide.

It is recommended that the drawing sheet be fixed to the board by means of clips or tape, not drawing pins which will damage the board.

The large boards will have some form of mounting. This enables the operator to move the board quickly and easily to any position so that work can be comfortably accomplished at any point on the board's surface.

To enable lines to be drawn horizontally and parallel to one another a blade is placed across the board. In the original form this was in the shape of a tee, the blade being fairly thin with a bevelled edge attached to a short stock at right angles. The stock would run up and down the working edge of the board. The blade would be of wood or plastic, this latter material enabling the draughtsperson to see the part of the drawing covered by the blade. (See Fig. 2.1.)

On large drawing boards the tee square is replaced by a blade fitted to a pulley system. This allows the blade to run up and down the board with parallel motion but will not fall off when the board is in a near vertical position.

A later development saw the introduction of an arm across the board. At the working end of this arm are mounted two high quality rules at right angles to each other. These can be rotated over the board's surface in increments of 15 degrees. This enables measurements to be made and angles to be drawn a little quicker. (See Fig. 2.2.)

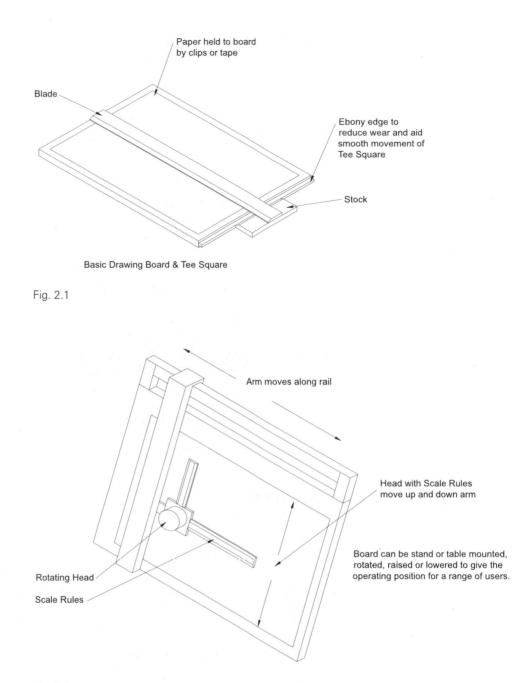

Fig. 2.1

Fig. 2.2

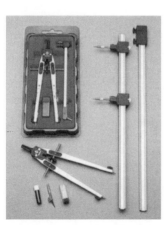

Fig. 2.3

Drawing instruments

These are traditionally seen as the instruments to draw circles, although many also regard the set squares and rule as instruments.

The instruments can be divided into those that draw small circles up to about 20 mm radius (small springbows), those that draw circles from about 5 mm radius up to about 150 mm radius (large springbows or dividers) and those that can be made to draw radii up to the maximum the drawing board can take (beam compass).

Taking cost into consideration a drawing instrument set may consist of a small springbow and a pair of dividers. These can usually take a point and a pencil lead or two points plus a small beam attachment to increase the maximum size of the radius that it can produce.

Fig. 2.4

Measuring instruments

This is usually seen as the scale rule, although there is a wide range from which to select. Consideration should be given to quality when looking at this instrument as this will be reflected in its accuracy and thus the accuracy of the drawing produced. This means that cost usually does reflect accuracy.

In this country you may still find scale rules with both millimetre and inch markings as well as those that give measurements to a set scale, i.e. 10:1, 50:1 100:1 etc. The choice is yours.

Fig. 2.5

Set squares

Traditionally there are two, the 60°, 30° set square and the 45° set square. These are made of clear plastic enabling the user to see the lines of the drawing underneath. It is recommended that the very small sizes be avoided.

An alternative used by many drawing office personnel is the adjustable set square. This is based on the 45° set square with the longest side being hinged at one end and a quadrant fitted enabling a wide range of angles to be set with reasonable accuracy.

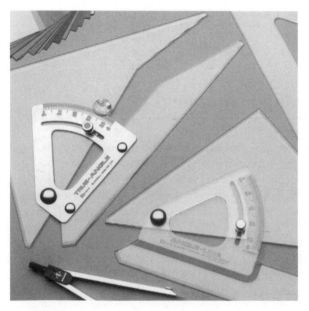

Fig. 2.6

Pencil and eraser

The range of pencils available are from 9H (very hard) to H, F, HB, B to 6B (very soft). The choice of pencil will depend on the user and the material on which the drawing is being made. Usually those used will be a hard pencil (about 2H) for setting out and construction work but used with a very light hand. For the final copy an HB or B (or even softer) will be used to obtain the quality of line required. This type of pencil will require continuous sharpening (usually trimming the end by rubbing on a glass paper block) to ensure the correct line thickness is obtained.

The eraser will feel soft and flexible. It will be able to remove the pencil marks without a great deal of rubbing and effort. If effort is required it is likely that some of the surface of the drawing sheet will be removed and this may cause marks to appear on the copy.

In both cases it is recommended that care is taken when purchasing; the cheapest may not give the quality required and the most expensive may be very costly.

Instruments to aid the drawing of curves

Many will see these as 'french curves'. These, in the basic form, are a set of four or five plastic shapes with predefined curves to match the helix, ellipse etc., see Fig 2.7. In some industries sets consisting of less complex shapes but a greater number of curves will be available for use by the whole office. The use of these to obtain a true shape and good curve is dependent on the skill and experience of the operator.

An alternative to these curves are long thin flexible strips of plastic with an L-shaped cross-section. These can be placed on the plotted points of the curve and held in position by special **weights**. Again these need practice to obtain a true shaped curve.

Fig. 2.7

1 Mount a sheet of drawing paper on the drawing board and draw five very faint parallel horizontal lines 100 mm long 10 mm apart using a 2H pencil.

2 Repeat the exercise in question 1, but using an H pencil. Ensure you obtain lines which are very black with a constant width of 0.5 mm.

3 Repeat the exercise again using an HB, or softer, pencil ensuring that the lines are very black with a constant width of 0.5 mm.

4 Using a soft eraser try removing one or two of the lines in questions 2 and 3.

Chapter 3

The engineering drawing sheet and its layout

The purpose of this chapter is to give the student some knowledge and understanding of the drawing sheet and its layout by:

- Giving details of the recommended drawing sheet sizes.
- Looking at the range of drawing sheet material available.
- Investigating the information required on the drawing sheet.
- Developing a sheet layout.

Drawing sheet sizes

These will usually be of the 'A' series. (It should be noted that some companies adopt their own range of sizes.) The 'A' series is based on a rectangle of one square metre with its sides in the ratio of $1:\sqrt{2}$. This is best demonstrated by means of a diagram and table, see Fig. 3.1.

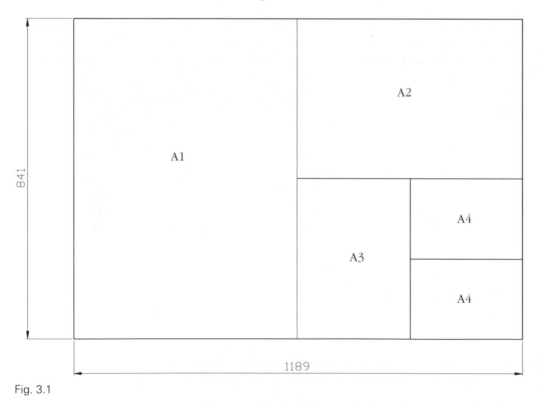

A size	Dimensions
A0	1189 × 841
A1	841 × 594
A2	594 × 420
A3	420 × 297
A4	297 × 210

Fig. 3.1

Drawing sheet material

Drawings can be produced on paper, linen, and plastic film. These are available in roll and single-sheet form. In single-sheet form the sizes will conform to the size series adopted by the company and may be preprinted with the standard layout used by the company.

Costs and what is being drawn will determine the material being used. To illustrate this two extreme examples are:

- A rough layout will probably use relatively cheap paper.
- A final drawing which may have to be microfilmed (i.e. the making of a 35 mm slide of the whole drawing) and have many copies made from it will be drawn on plastic film.

Plastic film has become very popular over recent years (both in the traditional and in the computer-aided drawing office). This has a number of distinct advantages:

- A better drawing surface formulated for both pen or pencil.
- Far better dimensional stability (i.e. pressure on its surface will not produce stretching).
- Better wear characteristics (i.e. will withstand storage and resist continual corrections).
- Less change due to moisture and temperature.
- Better copying capabilities.

When considering these and that the bulk of the costs of a drawing are attributable to personnel, film can be seen to be more economical than paper.

Drawing sheet layout

The drawing sheet, as has already been mentioned, can be pre-prepared with a border, title block etc. This will apply to both the traditional and the computer-aided office. The design of the layout of the sheet and what is included will be very much a company decision but British Standards (BS 308) gives very clear guidance in this area. See Fig. 3.2.

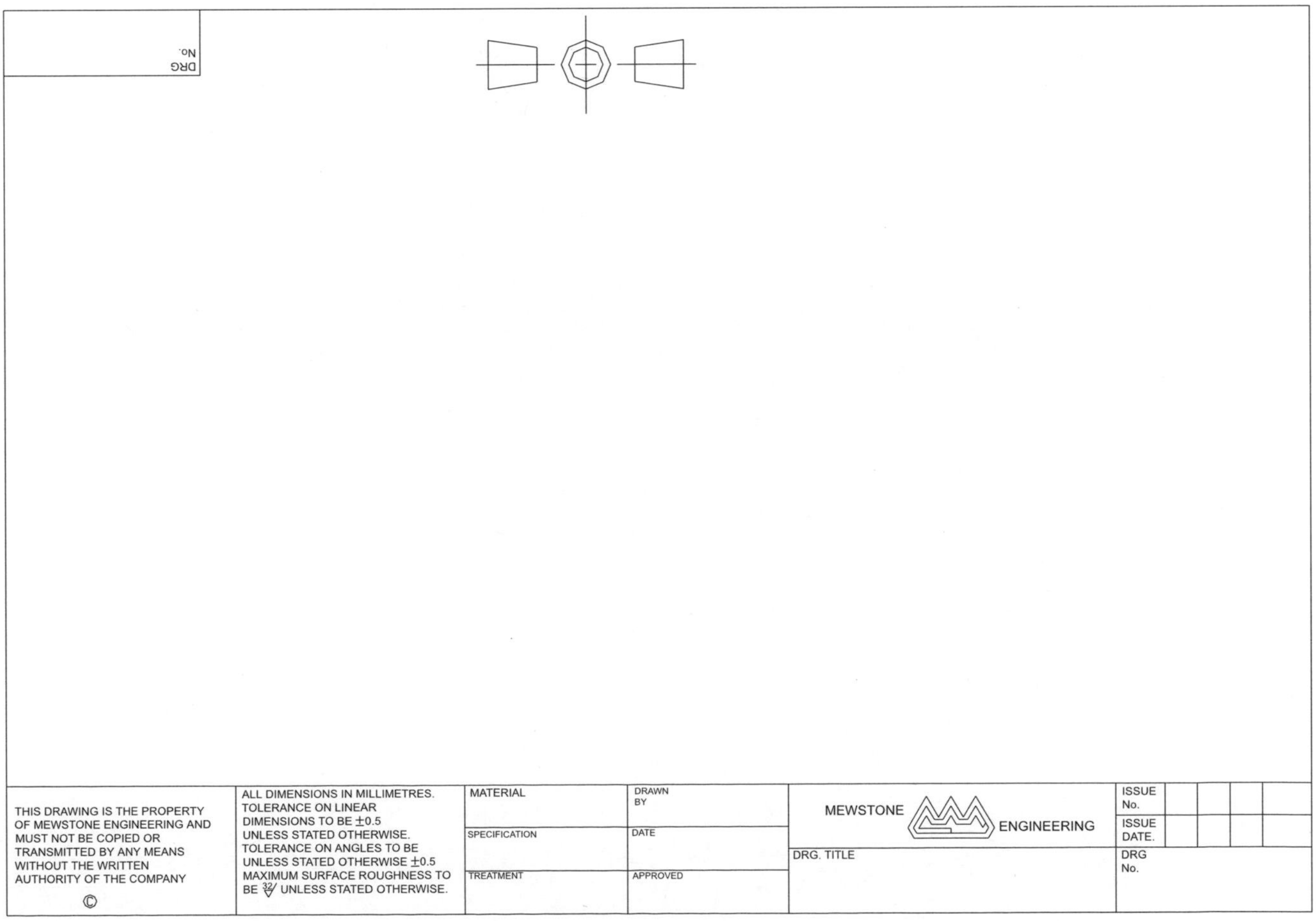

Fig. 3.2

Some of the items suggested for inclusion by BS 308 are: company name and logo, copyright note, issue number, date of issue, date drawn, drawn by, approval signature, projection, title, drawing number, material specification, reference to other similar parts, surface finish, surface roughness, heat treatment. There are more listed in BS 308.

Exercises

1 Prepare an A3 drawing sheet with a border giving the basic details required within your course. (For example a small title block giving name, date, course, topic area etc.)

2 Prepare an A3 drawing sheet for use within your course when drawing an engineering component.

Chapter 4

Basic geometrical constructions

The purpose of this chapter is to introduce the student to the skills and knowledge required to produce most of the geometric constructions used in engineering drawing.

The constructions described are those which will enable the student to develop their draughting skills and are seen as:

- Division of lines and angles.
- Construction of tangents.
- Blending of radii.
- Ellipse construction.

Before attempting any drawing it is suggested that you read through each of the prepared examples and then reproduce the figures with the help and guidance of your lecturer. You should continually refer to the notes and diagram in each example.

Note that accuracy must be a key factor in all geometrical construction; inaccuracy will make the construction unusable.

Dividing a line into equal parts

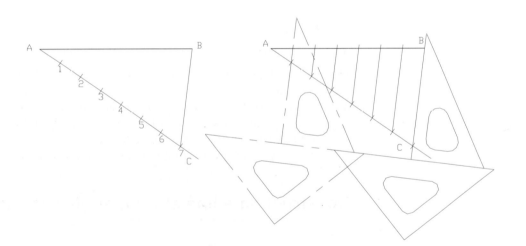

Fig. 4.1

A line AB is 126 mm long and is to be divided into seven equal parts.

1. Draw the line AB accurately to a length of 126 mm. (It does not have to be exactly horizontal.)
2. Draw a line AC at any convenient angle and length.
3. Using dividers set to a convenient distance mark off accurately the number of divisions required, in this case seven.
4. Using a straight edge join the point C on the line AC with the point B on the line AB thus forming the line BC.
5. Draw lines parallel to BC through each of the points marked out on the line AC through AB using the method shown in Fig. 4.1.

Note: The line AB may be divided into a ratio of parts, in the example above this could be 4:3. This would mean that only line 4 need be drawn parallel to BC.

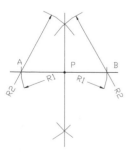

Bisecting a straight line

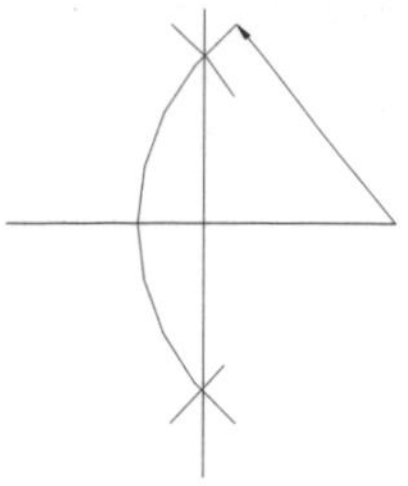

A line 90 mm long is to be divided into two equal parts.

1. Draw a line 90 mm long using a straight edge, not a tee square; it does not have to be horizontal.
2. Set your dividers to a radius of about three quarters the length of the line.
3. Accurately place the point of the dividers on one end of the line and draw an arc from above to below the line ensuring that ends of the arc are across the centre of the line.
4. Repeat this process at the other end of the line, ensuring the arcs intersect.
5. Draw a line through the intersection of the arcs ensuring that the line passes through both arcs accurately.

The vertical line drawn will pass through the centre of the original line.

Fig. 4.2

Bisecting an angle

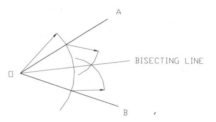

Fig. 4.3

An angle of about 25° is required to be divided into two equal parts.

1. Draw two lines to form an angle similar to the one shown in Fig. 4.3. The size of the angle is unimportant as the same principles apply to all angles.
2. Using dividers draw an arc of any radius from the intersect of the two lines (point 0).
3. From the point of intersection of the arc with each of the lines that form the angle describe an arc ensuring that they intersect.
4. Draw a line which passes through this arc and point 0 to obtain the bisecting line.

Constructing a line at right angles at a desired point

A line is required to be drawn at right angles through a given line at a specific point. Draw a line AB 130 mm long. A line perpendicular to AB is required at point P which is 75 mm to the right of A on the line AB.

1. Draw a line using a straight edge (not a tee square) 130 mm long and mark a point P 75 mm from A on AB.
2. Set the dividers to any radius (R1) and accurately produce arcs on the line AB using point P as the centre. The size of the radius R1 is not important. (*Note*: The radius R1 should not be too small as this will increase the chance of inaccuracy.)
3. Set the dividers to about three quarters the distance between the arcs you have just produced to give Radius R2. (*Note*: The procedure described in 2, 3 and 4 is similar to the exercise for bisecting a straight line.)
4. Place the dividers on the left-hand arc and describe arcs above and below the given line; repeat this for the right-hand arc. Ensure the arcs intersect above and below the given line.
5. Draw a line through the arcs and point P. (*Note*: One pair of the arcs, top or bottom, may be omitted if conformation of the accuracy is not required.)

Fig. 4.4

Drawing a tangent to a circle at a given point

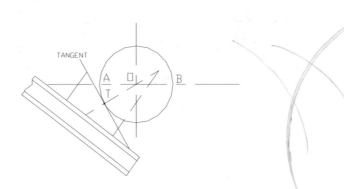

Fig. 4.5

O is the centre of the given circle of 50 mm diameter and C is the point at which the tangent is required. (Make this about 30° below the horizontal; an exact position is not required.)

1. After drawing accurately the circle and establishing point C use a set square and a straight edge, which may be another set square, arranged in such a way that the longer side of the set square passes through the centre of the circle and the point of tangency T. Draw a line through points O and T.
2. Holding the straight edge firmly in place turn the set square until the long side passes through C. (This usually means turning the set square through 90°.)
3. An alternative to the above method is to construct a line at right angles to the line OT at point T (as given for construction of a line at right angles at a desired point).
4. Draw a line along the set square through C; this is the tangent required.

Drawing a tangent to a circle from a point outside the circle

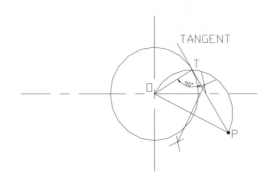

Fig. 4.6

Draw a circle 60 mm diameter and place the point P at a position about 60 mm radius and 30° below the horizontal.

1. Draw a line from the centre of the given circle to the point P.
2. Bisect the line OP as detailed in construction for bisecting a straight line, and draw a semi-circle with length OP as the diameter.
3. Draw a line from the centre of the circle (O) to the point at which the semi-circle cuts the circle; this is the point of tangency T. Draw a line joining point P through point T for the tangent.

Drawing a tangent to two given circles

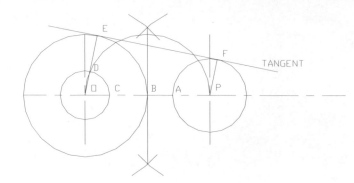

Fig. 4.7

Draw two circles of radius OB = 50 mm and PA = 30 mm. The distance between centres is 100 mm.

1. Draw a line joining the centres of the two given circles giving the line OP.
2. Bisect the line OP and with this as the diameter draw a semi-circle.
3. Draw a circle with centre O whose radius is the difference of the radii of the two given circles (in this case OB − PA = OC, or 25 − 15 = 10).
4. Draw a line from the centre of the circle OC through the point at which the semi-circle cuts this circle giving point D and extend it to cut the circle OB giving point E. This is the point of tangency on this circle.
5. Draw a line parallel to OE from centre P to produce the line PF. This gives the point of tangency at F on this circle.
6. Produce the tangent EF by drawing a line through the points E and F accurately.

Drawing a circle tangential to two straight lines

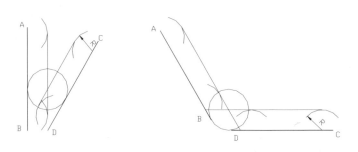

Fig. 4.8

Draw two lines to produce an acute angle of approximately 30° as shown in the left-hand figure, and two lines to produce an obtuse angle approximately of 120°. The lines are shown as AB and CD.

A circle of 20 mm diameter is required to be drawn to touch but not cut the lines AB and CD

1. Draw a line parallel to AB and CD by setting the dividers to the radius required (i.e. 20 mm) and draw arcs from any two points along each line. With great care draw a line to touch but not cut the arcs. The intersection of these lines is the centre of the required radius.
2. Draw the arc required from the centre just determined.

Drawing an arc of given radius to two given circles

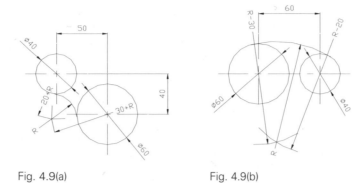

Fig. 4.9(a)   Fig. 4.9(b)

Draw carefully the circles shown in Fig. 4.9(a) and 4.9(b). R = 25 mm in Fig. 4.9(a) and R = 100 mm in Fig. 4.9(b).

The method is similar with the only difference being either the addition or subtraction of the radii. Using Fig. 4.9(a):

1. From the centre point of the large circle draw an arc of a radius equal to the radius of the arc required *plus* the radius of the circles whose centre is being used (i.e. 30 mm + 25 mm = 55 mm).
2. Repeat the above procedure to describe an arc from the centre of the second circle (the radius being 20 mm + 25 mm = 45 mm).
3. The intersection of the two arcs is the centre point of the 25 radius required to draw an arc tangential to the two circles. Draw in an arc that touches but does not cut the two circles; check its size.

Using Fig. 4.9(b):

1. From the centre point of the small circle describe an arc of a radius equal to the radius of the arc required *minus* the radius of the circles whose centre is being used (the radius being 100 mm − 20 mm = 80 mm).
2. Repeat the above procedure to describe an arc from the centre of the second circle whose centre point is marked P (the radius being 100 mm − 30 mm = 70 mm).
3. The intersection of the two arcs is the centre point of the 100 radius required to draw an arc tangential to the two circles. Draw in an arc that touches but does not cut the two circles; check its size.

Constructing an ellipse

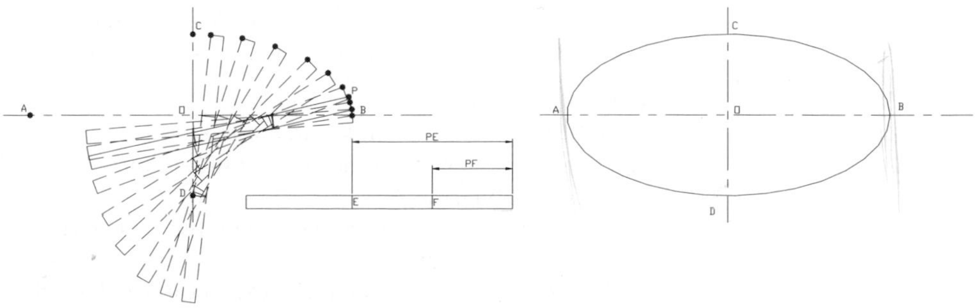

Fig. 4.10

If a point moves according to mathematically defined conditions a curve known as a **locus** is produced. The ellipse is one of these curves.

There are many methods of constructing an ellipse; the method described below is known as the **trammel method**.

An ellipse consists of a curve and two straight lines; the straight lines are known as the axes. The longer line is the major axis (AB) and the shorter the minor axis (CD). The length of the major axis (AB) is 90 mm and the length of the minor axis is 40 mm.

1. Draw the major and minor axes and mark out accurately the lengths of each axis.
2. Using a strip of thin fairly stiff cardboard mark on lengths equal to half the major and minor axes; in Fig. 4.10 these are shown as the length PE, which equals half the major and the length PF which equals half the minor axis.
3. Drawing a quarter of the ellipse at a time, place the strip across the axes in such a way as to place the point E on the minor axis and F on the major axis and record this position by placing a dot at the point P on the drawing.
4. Repeat this process for as many dots as are required to give the quarter shape of the ellipse.
5. Join the dots carefully with a freehand drawn arc.
6. Repeat this process for each of the remaining sections of the ellipse.

Constructing an ellipse (concentric circles method)

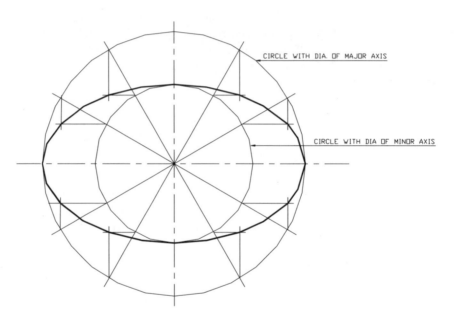

CIRCLE WITH DIA. OF MAJOR AXIS

CIRCLE WITH DIA OF MINOR AXIS

Fig. 4.11

This is a simpler, but is regarded as a less accurate method of drawing an ellipse. The major axis = 150 mm and the minor axis = 90 mm.

1. Draw two circles on a common axis. The radii of each circle should correspond to half the major and half the minor axis.
2. Draw accurately from the centre of the concentric circles radial lines at 30° and 60° across both circles.
3. Where the radial lines intersect with the large circle (radius equal to the major axis) draw a short vertical line.
4. Where the radial lines intersect with the small circle (radius equal to the minor axis) draw a short horizontal line. (Ensure that these vertical and horizontal lines intersect.)
5. Draw **freehand** a smooth curve through the intersections just produced.
6. You may add additional radial lines at 15°, 45° and 75° and the appropriate vertical and horizontal lines to give extra **points** thus providing a more accurate curve.

Note: All construction lines should be shown.

1 Draw a horizontal line 135 mm long and divide it into the ratio of 1:3:3.

2 Construct the following angles using a straight edge and dividers only: 90°, 60°, 45° and 15°.

3 Draw a 50 mm diameter circle and a 35 mm diameter circle with 150 mm between centres. Construct a tangent to both circles.

4 Draw accurately the figure shown in Fig. 4.12.

5 Construct an ellipse with a major axis of 100 mm and a minor axis of 60 mm using the two circle method.

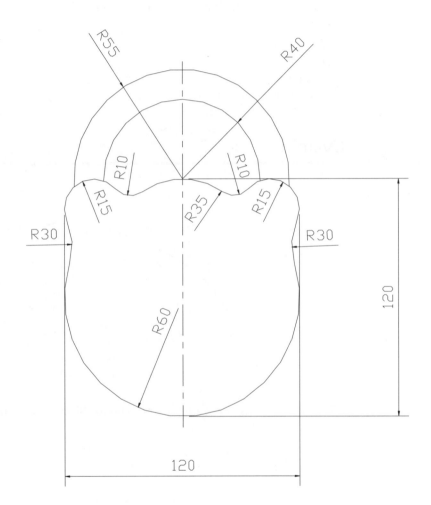

Fig. 4.12

Chapter 5

Advanced and applied geometrical constructions

The purpose of this chapter is to give the student the knowledge, understanding and some practical ability in the use of some of the advanced geometrical constructions.

This is done by using previously introduced geometrical construction techniques together with new techniques to produce the following:

- Cycloid.
- Locus of a point on a mechanism.
- Helix.
- Cam construction.
- Cam follower motions.

Cycloid

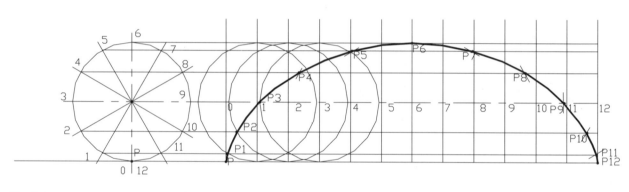

Fig. 5.1

When a circle rolls along a flat plane without slipping, a point on the circumference will describe a path known as a cycloid.

1. Draw the circle of 50 mm diameter, and divide it into 12 equal parts numbering them anti-clockwise starting with 0 at the bottom vertical point, also mark this point as P.
2. Extend the horizontal centre line out to the right-hand side.
3. Draw a vertical line about 15 mm to the right of the circle. Measure off a length equal to the circumference of the circle along the centre line.
4. Divide this distance into 12 equal parts as demonstrated in Chapter 4, p. 15. Number each point from the left starting at 0 and ending with 12.
5. Draw horizontal lines to the right through the points (0,12) (1,11) (2,10) etc. as shown in Fig. 5.1.
6. With the dividers set to the radius of the rolling circle (25 mm) place the point at the position marked 1 on the horizontal line drawn through (3,9) (the centre line of the rolling circle) and draw an arc which cuts the horizontal line (1,11). (This will be very close to the vertical line.)
7. Place the dividers on point 2 on the centre line and describe an arc which cuts the horizontal line 2,10.
8. Continue with this using points 3, 4 and 5. The arc from point 6 will just touch the horizontal line vertically above point 6.

9. To obtain the next point from position 7, place the dividers on point 7 and describe an arc on line 5,7 and ensure that it is to the right of point 7. This ensures that the circle is continuing to roll to the right.
10. Continue to plot the points 8 to 11 and ensure that they are to the right of the dividers point.
11. On completion of plotting the points draw a curve through all the points **freehand**.

Locus of a point on a mechanism

In this book the number of links is limited to four.

Locus of a point on a mechanism of two links

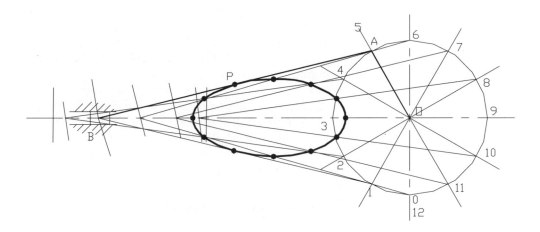

Fig. 5.2

In this mechanism a crank OA rotates clockwise about O. A connecting rod AB is attached by a pivot at B which slides along the axis OB. Point P is the mid-point of the connecting rod AB.

1. Draw a horizontal line and place a circle of 60 mm diameter at the right-hand side and mark the centre as O.
2. Divide the circle into 12 equal parts and number them 0–12 as in the cycloid.
3. From point 5 with the dividers set to 110 mm draw an arc on the horizontal centre line to the left of the circle.
4. Label point 5 as A and the point of intersection of the arc with the horizontal centre line as B. Draw a line through A to B. Mark the point P. This is mid-way between A and B (i.e. AP = BP = 55 mm).
5. The point B is free to slide along the line OB.
6. With the dividers set to the distance AB mark off point B on the horizontal line for each of the positions on the circle.
7. Mark on the rod AB the point P. (You may find it less confusing to plot point P as you draw in each line AB.)
8. Draw a freehand curve through all the points plotted.

Plotting the locus of a point which appears outside a mechanism

In this mechanism a crank OA rotates about O clockwise. A connecting rod is joined to the crank at A; the rod slides freely through a fixed pivot block at B. The rod is extended at both ends to give the points C and D.

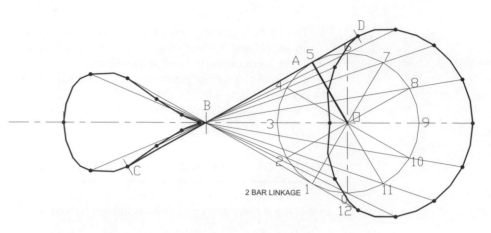

Fig. 5.3

The locus of points C and D are required.

1. Draw a circle of radius 40 mm. Divide the circle into 12 equal parts and number them as before.
2. Mark a point on an extended centre line of the circle 80 mm from the circle centre to the left of the circle (this is the position of the fixed pivoted sliding block). Label this point B.
3. Draw a line through point 5 (label this point A) and the point B. Mark off a length of 120 mm along this line and label the end as C. Extend this line beyond A to the right by 30 mm and label this point as D.
4. Using this method of construction draw a connecting rod at each of the points on the circle and mark in each of the points C and D.
5. Draw a freehand curve through the points plotted for C and D.

Toggle action mechansim

In this mechanism the crank OA rotates about O clockwise. The connecting rods AB and BC are pivoted at A, B and C but the pivot C is fixed. Point D is a fixed pivot which is allowed to slide along the horizontal.

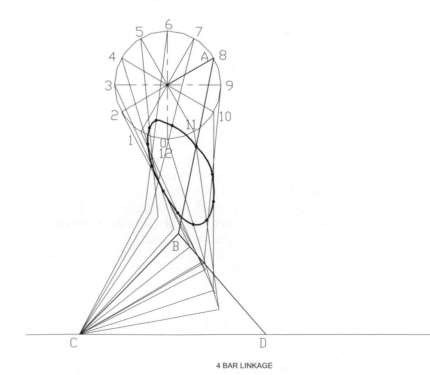

4 BAR LINKAGE

Fig. 5.4

This construction follows the methods used in the previous two sections.

1. Draw a circle of 80 mm diameter and divide it into 12 equal parts. Make position 8 as A.
2. Draw a horizontal line 140 mm below the horizontal centre line of the circle.
3. Point C is 50 mm to the left of the vertical centre line of the circle on the lower horizontal line. Point D slides along this line.
4. Draw an arc of 80 mm radius with the centre C.
5. Draw an arc from A of radius 100 mm to cut the arc about C. This gives the point B. Draw in BD with the dividers set to 75 mm and centre B.
6. Point P is the mid-point of AB (i.e. AP = BP = 50 mm).
7. Construct each position carefully and determine the position of point P.
8. Draw a freehand curve through all points P.

Helix

The helix is of importance in the construction of the screw threads, springs, worm gearing and cylindrical cams.

It may be considered as the path followed by a point moving horizontally with uniform velocity along a cylinder while the cylinder rotates about its axis with uniform velocity. This sounds very complex but a simpler explanation (but not as accurate) could be: a line traced out on a cylinder by a point when it moves round and along the cylinder at constant velocities.

A helix is required to be drawn with a cylinder diameter of 100 mm and a lead of 50 mm (i.e. this is the distance moved forward by the point at constant velocity in one revolution of the cylinder).

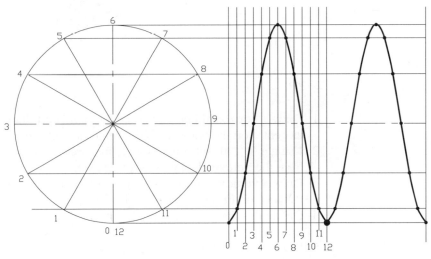

Fig. 5.5

1. Draw a horizontal line and at the left-hand end draw a circle 100 mm diameter with its centre on the line.
2. Using a 60°/30° set square divide the circle into twelve equal parts and number them from the bottom clockwise starting from 0.
3. Draw a vertical line just to the right of the circle. From this line mark off a horizontal distance of 50 mm. (This is the lead.)
4. Divide this distance into 12 equal parts and number them from the left starting from 0.
5. Draw horizontal lines through the points where the circle division lines cut the circle and extend them through the 50 mm distance just drawn (i.e. (0,12), (1,11), (2,10), (3,9), the centre line etc.).

6. Where horizontal line 0 cuts vertical line 0 mark clearly the point.
7. Where horizontal line 1 cuts vertical line 1 mark clearly the point.
8. Repeat this till all 12 points are marked. This is the path of the point around the cylinder.
9. Mark off a second lead (i.e. mark off 50 mm to the right of the last plotted point). Extend all horizontal lines through this distance.
10. Using a divider set to 50 mm mark off this distance from each of the points along each line. This will produce a second turn of the helix.
11. Draw in the curve freehand.

Spring construction

This follows a similar construction method to the basic helix.

A spring with an external diameter of 90 mm and a lead of 40 mm, the wire diameter being 10 mm, is required.

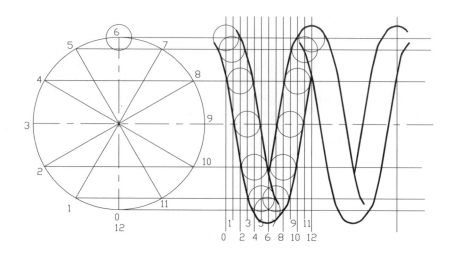

Fig. 5.6

1. Draw a horizontal line and at the left-hand end draw a circle 80 mm diameter with its centre on the line (this is the centre line of the wire).
2. Using a 60°/30° set square divide the circle into 12 equal parts and number them from the bottom clockwise, starting from 0.
3. Draw a vertical line just to the right of the circle. From this line mark off a horizontal distance of 40 mm. (This is the lead.)
4. Divide this distance into 12 equal parts and number them from the left starting from 0.
5. Draw horizontal lines through the points where the circle division lines cut the circle and extend them through the 40 mm distance just drawn (i.e. (0,12), (1,11), (2,10), (3,9) the centre line etc.).
6. Where horizontal line 0 cuts vertical line 0 mark clearly the point.
7. Where horizontal line 1 cuts vertical line 1 mark clearly the point.
8. Repeat this till all 12 points are marked. This is the path of the point round the cylinder.
9. Mark off a second lead (i.e. mark off 40 mm to the right of the last plotted point). Extend all horizontal lines through this distance.
10. Using a divider set to 40 mm mark off this distance from each of the points along each line. This will produce a second turn of the helix.
11. On each of the points plotted draw a circle of 10 mm diameter.
12. Using a soft pencil, draw a curve tangential to the circles to produce the spring; reference should be made to Fig. 5.6. **This is a right-hand helix**.

Square thread

The construction for the square thread is similar to those already detailed. It should be noted that this is not difficult but all the construction lines may create confusion.

A helix must be constructed for the top of the thread and a helix for the bottom of the thread, this is shown in Fig 5.7.

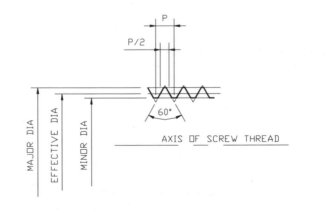

Fig. 5.7

Vee form thread

At this stage it is not necessary to construct a vee form thread but this could be done by using the techniques just described. In Fig. 5.8 the basic thread dimensions are shown and Fig. 5.9 shows how this would look when drawn fully using the techniques described.

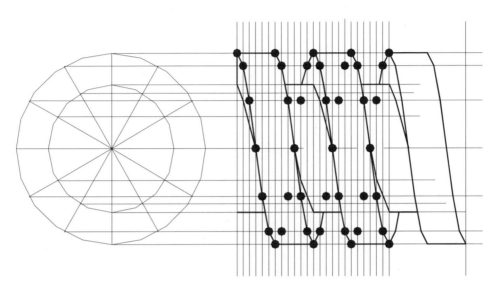

Fig. 5.8

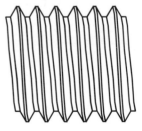

Fig. 5.9

Cam construction

A cam is generally a disc or cylinder mounted on a rotating shaft which gives a special motion to a follower that is in direct contact. The cam profile is determined by the motion that the follower is required to make.

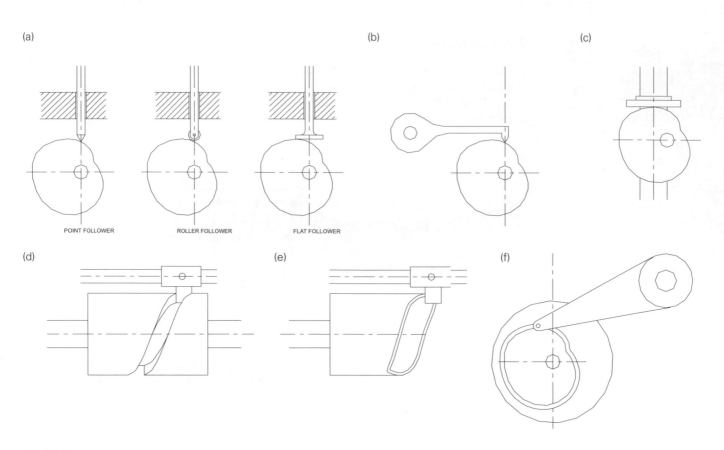

(a) (b) (c)

POINT FOLLOWER ROLLER FOLLOWER FLAT FOLLOWER

(d) (e) (f)

Fig. 5.10

Probably the most widely used cam is the plate cam which has its contour around the circumference. The line of action of the follower is usually vertical or parallel to the camshaft. Figure 5.10(a) shows a plate cam with a point, roller and flat followers. Figure 5.10(b) shows a plate cam with an offset point follower. Figure 5.10(c) shows a plate cam with an offset flat follower. Figure 5.10(d) shows a cylindrical cam. Figure 5.10(e) is a face cylindrical cam and Fig. 5.10(f) is a face cam.

Cam follower motions

Cam followers can be given a number of different motions dependent on what action the cam is designed to initiate. These motions are seen as:

- **Uniform velocity**
  This motion makes the followers rise or fall at constant speed (sometimes referred to as straight line motion). See Fig. 5.11(a).
- **Uniform acceleration and retardation**
  The shape of the curve for this motion is parabolic. Figure 5.11(b) shows its shape and construction.
- **Simple harmonic motion**
  The construction of this motion involves the drawing of a semi-circle and dividing into the same number of parts as the cam displacement angle. The diameter of the semi-circle is equal to the rise, or fall, of the follower. See Fig. 5.11(c).

The construction of a cam is complex and should be looked on as a combination exercise to be embarked on only when all other exercises have been completed. You may also require the help of your lecturer.

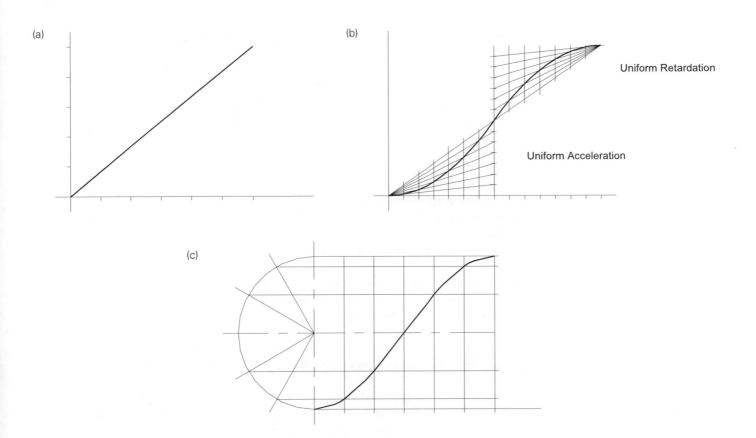

(a)

(b) Uniform Retardation

Uniform Acceleration

(c)

Fig. 5.11

The cam to be constructed has the following specification:

- Plate cam rotating anti-clockwise with a point follower. (Direction of rotation dictates the direction of plotting the curve.)
- Least radius of the cam is 20 mm.
- Camshaft diameter 10 mm.
- 0–90° a rise of 10 mm with uniform velocity.
- 90–150° a rise of 10 mm with simple harmonic motion.
- 150–210° dwell.
- 210–285° a fall of 10 mm with uniform acceleration.
- 285–360° a fall of 10 mm with uniform retardation.

(*Note*: All lines should be drawn fairly faint at the start as you may find you make errors. All instructions overleaf refer to Fig. 5.12.)

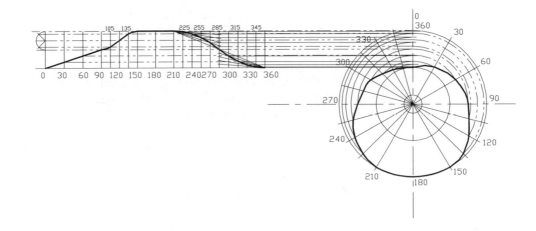

Fig. 5.12

1. Draw the horizontal and vertical centre lines of the cam and the circle representing the cam shaft.
2. Draw on the same centre the circle representing the least radius and a circle representing the maximum radius that the cam is to operate at, e.g. the minimum radius is 20 mm and the maximum radius is 40 mm radius. (These represent the minimum and maximum distances of the follower from the centre of the cams rotation.)
3. Divide the circles into 12 equal parts and mark on the number of degrees **clockwise** starting from the top vertical centre line. If more plotting points are required more radial lines can be added later.
4. The **cam graph** must now be constructed. Draw two horizontal lines out to the left from the intersection of the minimum and maximum radius circles with the vertical centre line at the top.
5. At a convenient point out to the left draw a vertical line across the two horizontal lines just drawn. From this line draw 12 equi-spaced lines to the left of this line with a spacing of 10 mm. Number these 0–360° with the left-hand point being 0°. These represent the radial lines drawn on the cam. As with the radial lines it may be necessary to add more later as required.

At this stage you might find it a help to construct each part of the cam graph and plot the cam before proceeding with the next stage. It may help to avoid some confusion.

6. The first part of the graph is uniform velocity. Draw a line 10 mm above the line extended from the minimum radius of the cam.
7. Join the point 0° and the point where the 10 mm line just drawn intersects with the 90° vertical line position with a straight line.
8. Draw vertical lines to cut this angled line from the 30° and 60° points.
9. Where these lines intersect draw horizontal lines to the right till they cut the vertical centre line through the cam.
10. Using dividers, from the cam centre draw arcs from each of these lines till they cut their appropriate radial line.
11. The second movement is a rise of 10 mm with simple harmonic motion between 90° and 150°. This requires the addition of lines representing 105° and 135° on the cam graph and on the cam.
12. Divide the rise of 10 mm into two and draw a horizontal line. Using this line as a centre line draw a semi-circle at a convenient point and divide into four equal parts (use a 45° set square). You may find it helpful to mark these 90°, 105°, 120°, 135° and 150°.
13. Draw a horizontal line across the graph from the intersection of these lines with the semi-circle till they meet the correct vertical line. Plot the curve on the cam graph. Plot these positions on the cam as before.
14. The next movement of the follower is a dwell from 150–210°. This is a straight line on the cam graph and is a radius on the cam and therefore can be drawn with dividers.
15. The next two sections representing a fall of 10 mm with uniform acceleration and a fall of 10 mm with uniform retardation can be plotted as one on the cam graph. Additional lines are required at 225°, 255°, 285°, 315° and 345° on the cam and the cam graph.
16. Divide the vertical line at 285° on the cam graph into 10 equal parts. Then follow the method of plotting the points as illustrated in Fig. 5.11(b). Draw in the curve on the cam graph and then plot out the points on the cam.
17. Draw in the curve on the cam.

Exercises

1 Construct the path of a point on the rim of a wheel of 60 mm diameter as it rolls for one complete revolution, without slipping, along a flat surface.

2 In Fig. 5.13 the link OA rotates about O and C is a pivot. Plot the path of P and Q for one revolution of the rod. OA = 40, AP = 35, AQ = 150.

3 A helix has a cylinder diameter of 85 mm and a lead of 25 mm. Construct the helix.

4 A plate cam has the following characteristics:
- Clockwise rotation.
- 20 mm dia in line roller follower.
- Minimum distance of roller from the cam shaft centre is 50 mm.
- Cam shaft diameter 25 mm.
- 0–120° follower rises 28 mm with uniform acceleration.
- 120–210° follower rises 28 mm with uniform retardation.
- 210–240° dwell.
- 240–330° follower falls 56 mm with uniform velocity.
- 330–360° dwell.

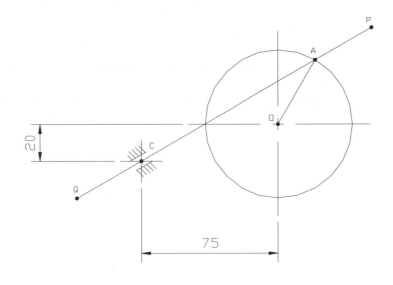

Fig. 5.13

Chapter 6

Development

It should be noted that this subject area requires the knowledge of orthographic projection. Students will find that it combines the subjects of geometrical construction and orthographic projection. The purpose of this chapter is to give the student knowledge and understanding of development of sheet material and its application to ducting and pipe work. The knowledge and understanding is given to the student by using the development of rectangular, hexagonal and cylindrical prisms, and cones.

This knowledge is developed further by adding a cutting plane to each shape and then applying these methods to ducting and pipe work. Many articles such as the car, computer bodies, air conditioning, pipe work and ducting are produced from sheet material and pipe work. To enable such articles to be manufactured it is essential to have a knowledge of what form the developments will take at various stages of manufacture.

A number of worked-through exercises follow. The development of the square and rectangle boxes illustrated should not be attempted as they are there to demonstrate the principle only. Both of these assume that there is a top and bottom but the rest of the exercises have no top and bottom.

Note: When drawing each of the work-through exercises produce all lines as you would for construction (i.e. faint); do not erase any of these lines.

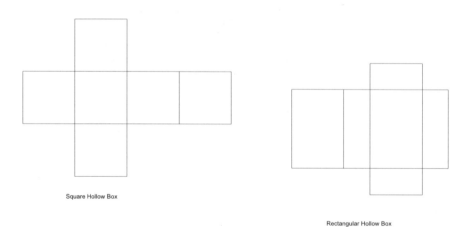

Square Hollow Box

Rectangular Hollow Box

Fig. 6.1

Hexagonal prism

1. Draw a hexagon which is 40 mm A/F with one pair of faces horizontal.
2. Above this hexagon produce a front elevation with a height of 80 mm as seen in Fig. 6.2.
3. Extend the lines forming the top and bottom of the front elevation to the right.
4. Draw a vertical line about 20 mm to the right of the front elevation cutting both the horizontal lines.
5. With dividers set to the length of a face of the hexagon step off six faces from the vertical line to the right of the front elevation.
6. Using a soft pencil draw in the shape of the hexagon front elevation, plan and development.

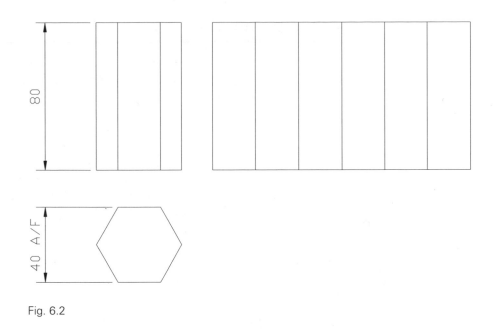

Fig. 6.2

Cylinder

1. Draw a circle of 40 mm diameter and divide it into 12 equal parts.
2. Produce a front elevation with a height of 80 mm.
3. Extend the lines from the top and bottom of the cylinder in the front elevation out to the left-hand side.
4. Draw a vertical line about 20 mm to the left of the front elevation cutting both the top and bottom horizontal lines.
5. Draw a second vertical line to the left of the first at a distance equal to the circumference of the cylinder. (You should make this as accurate as you can using the formulae πD where D = diameter of the cylinder.)
6. Using a soft pencil draw in the shape of the cylinder front elevation, plan and development.

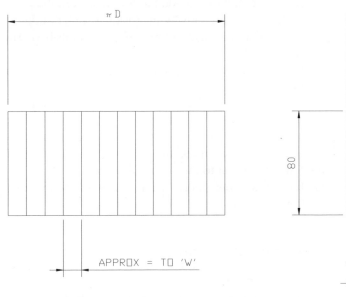

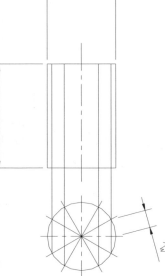

Fig. 6.3

Square pyramid

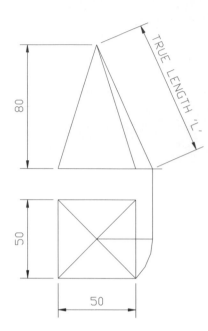
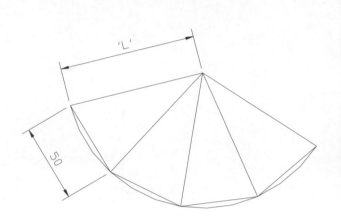

Fig. 6.4

1. Draw a square with a side length of 50 mm. Draw in the diagonals.
2. Draw a front elevation with a height of 80 mm.
3. To complete the development the actual or **true length** of the sloping edge of the pyramid is required. Draw a horizontal line on the plan from the centre of the pyramid out to the right.
4. With the dividers at the intersection of the diagonals in the plan draw an arc of radius equal to half the diagonal length till it touches the horizontal line drawn.
5. Draw a vertical line from the point where the arc touches the horizontal line in the plan up to a line extended to the right from the base of the pyramid.
6. In the front view draw a line, using a straight edge, from the top of the pyramid to the point to the right of the base just established. This is the **true length** of the sloping edge.
7. Set the true length on the dividers and draw an arc in a space out to the right of the front elevation.
8. Using a straight edge, draw a line from the centre of the arc to cut the arc near to one end.
9. Set the dividers to the length of one side of the base of the pyramid and set off four equal divisions on the arc.
10. Join each point to the centre of the arc.
11. Using a soft pencil draw in the shape of the pyramid front elevation, plan and development.

Hexagonal pyramid

Using the same method described in the development of the square pyramid. Make the hexagon 50 mm A/F and 80 mm in height.

Note: If you draw the hexagon with one pair of sides horizontal you will not have to determine the true length as the two of the edges will give the true length.

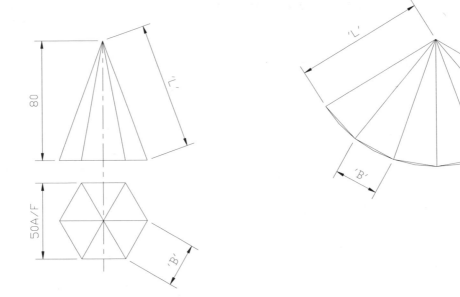

Fig. 6.5

Cone

Although this development is similar to those of the hexagonal and square pyramid there is significant differences which makes it necessary to go into detail.

1. Draw the plan and front elevation of a cone which has a base diameter of 40 mm and a height of 60 mm. Divide the plan into 12 equal parts.
2. With the dividers set to the length of the sloping side draw an arc on the right-hand side of the front view.
3. Using a straight edge draw a line from the arc centre to cut the arc near to one end.
4. Set the dividers to the length of one twelfth of the circumference from the plan, shown as distance B in Fig. 6.6.
5. Step this length off carefully round the arc 12 times and then join each point to the centre of the arc. (Although this length is approximate it is accepted as being accurate enough. You may determine the length of the arc mathematically if you wish.)
6. Using a soft pencil draw in the shape of the cone front elevation, plan and development.

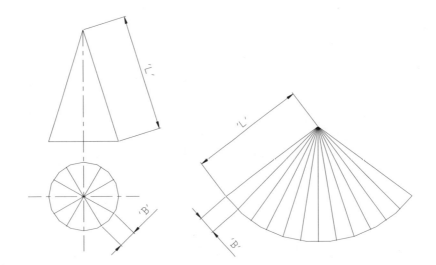

Fig. 6.6

Rectangular prism development with cutting plane

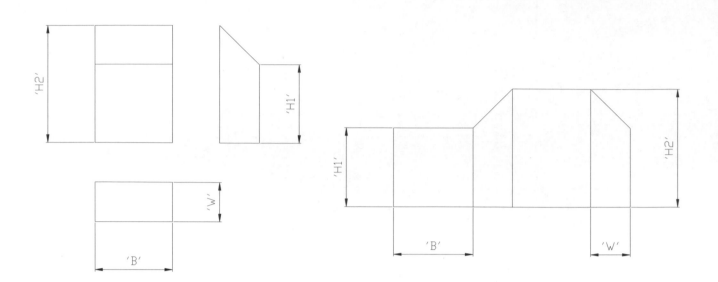

Fig. 6.7

Figure 6.7 shows the same rectangular prism as in Fig. 6.1. In Fig. 6.7 a **cutting plane** has been added (i.e. the item has been cut by slicing off the top at a particular point and angle).

This is fairly self explanatory and there is little need to work through this illustration, but if students feel they need the practice then draw it.

Note: The join is always taken as the shortest length, as in practice this affects the cost of manufacture.

Hexagonal prism development with cutting plane

1. Using the same dimensions as in Fig. 6.2 (i.e. 40 mm A/F with a height of 80 mm) draw a plan, front elevation and end elevation of the prism. (*Note*: To save time and paper you may, by adding an end elevation, produce the cutting plane and modify the development produced above for the hexagonal prism.)

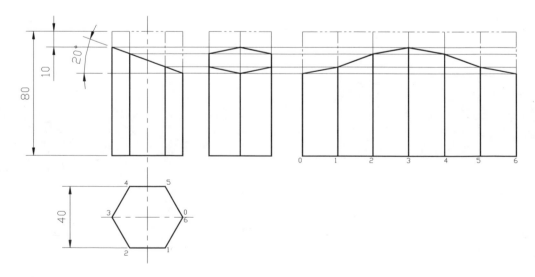

Fig. 6.8

2. Draw a line representing the cutting plane on the front elevation 10 mm down from the top left-hand side and at an angle of 20° sloping down to the right.
3. Draw the result produced by the cutting plane on the end elevation (i.e. draw horizontal lines from the intersection of the cutting plane with corners of the hexagon from the front elevation across to the end elevation and join the points plotted).
4. Draw the full development without taking the cutting plane into consideration.
5. Using dividers step off the distances from the base to the cutting plane for each corner. (Ensure that you start and end with the shortest line.)
6. Join up the points plotted out then using a soft pencil draw in the shape of the hexagonal prism front elevation, plan and development.

Cylindrical prism development with cutting plane

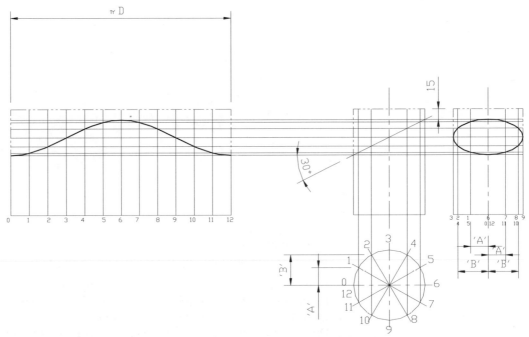

Fig. 6.9

As with the previous exercise you may wish to add the end elevation, cutting plane, construction lines and modify the development of the prism drawn in Fig. 6.3.

1. Draw the plan, front elevation and side elevation of the cylinder. Divide the plan into 12 equal parts.
2. Draw vertical lines across the front elevation from the point of intersection of each of the dividing lines with the diameter in the plan.
3. Draw the cutting plane in the front elevation 15 mm down on the right-hand side and at an angle of 30° sloping down to the left. Add numbers to the divisions in the plan ensuring that the line 0,12 represents the shortest line in the development.
4. Draw the full development of the cylinder as detailed above for the cylinder. Divide the length of the development into 12 equal parts using the technique given in Chapter 4 for division of a line into equal parts and then number each line from 0 to 12.
5. Draw horizontal lines across the development and the end elevation from the point of intersection of the vertical lines from the plan with the cutting plane in the front elevation.
6. Carefully plot out the curve on the development as shown in Fig. 6.9 and draw in the curve carefully.
7. Using dividers step off the distances shown in the plan given as 'A' and 'B' on the end elevation. Draw in the curve of the cut surface.
8. Using a soft pencil draw in the shape of the cylinder front elevation, plan and development.

Square pyramid with cutting plane

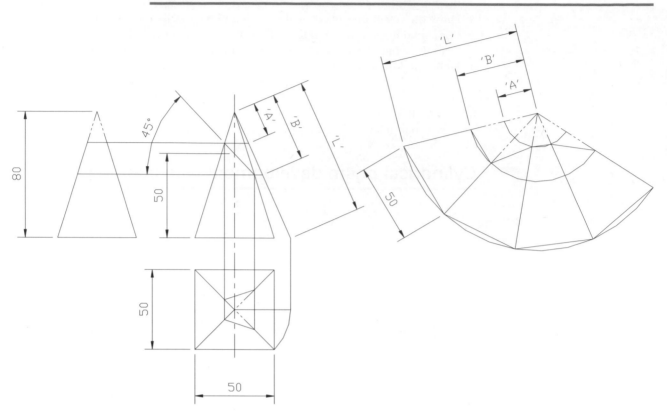

Fig. 6.10

As with the previous exercises you may wish to add the end elevation, cutting plane, construction lines and modify the development of the prism drawn in Fig. 6.4.

1. Draw the plan, front elevation and end elevation of the pyramid.
2. Determine the **true length** of the edge of the pyramid.
3. Draw the development of the full pyramid.
4. Draw in the cutting plane at a height of 50 mm on the centre line from the base and at an angle of 45° in the front elevation sloping down from the left to the right.
5. In the front elevation draw horizontal lines across from where the cutting plane cuts the edges to the true length line.
6. Using dividers transfer the lengths from the true length line to the development, as shown by the dimension's 'A' and 'B'.
7. From the front elevation draw lines horizontally across to the end elevation and vertically down to the plan.
8. Join the points where these lines cut there corresponding edges in these views to give the shape that will be seen.
9. Using a soft pencil draw in the shape of the pyramid, front elevation, plan and development.

Hexagonal pyramid with cutting plane

As with the previous exercises you may wish to add the end elevation, cutting plane, construction lines and modify the development of the prism drawn in Fig. 6.5.

1. Draw the plan, front elevation and end elevation of the pyramid.
2. Draw the full development of the pyramid.
3. Draw in the cutting plane which is to be at a height of 50 mm on the centre and at an angle of 40° sloping from left to right in the front elevation.

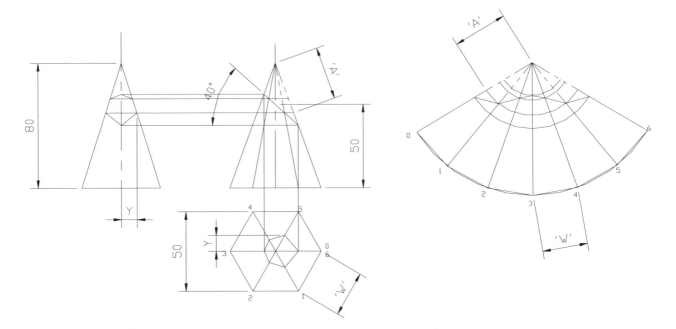

Fig. 6.11

4. Although the right-hand and left-hand edges of the front view are 'true lengths' the two inner edges are not. Therefore draw horizontal lines across from the point of intersection of the cutting plane with these edges till they cut the right-hand side.
5. Transfer the true lengths to the development using dividers (e.g. dimension 'A').
6. Draw lines from the front view to the plan and end elevation to allow the plotting of the cut shape in these views. Join the lines to give the shape that will be seen.
7. Using a soft pencil draw in the shape of the pyramid, front elevation, plan and development.

Cone with cutting plane

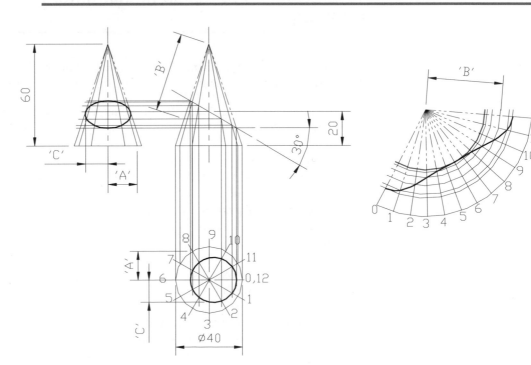

Fig. 6.12

Although it is possible to add this additional development to Fig. 6.6 it is advised that you draw it a second time to avoid confusion.

1. Draw the plan, front elevation, end elevation and development of the cone using the dimensions for the cone, above. These are a diameter of 40 mm and a height of 60 mm.
2. Divide the plan into 12 equal parts. Draw lines vertically from the intersection of the divisions with the diameter in the plan across the base line of the front elevation.
3. Draw a cutting plane at a height of 20 mm and an angle of 30° on the centre line of the front elevation. (It is advised that you now number the divisions in the plan and development ensuring the (0,12) is the shortest line in the front elevation.)
4. Using a straight edge draw lines in the front elevation from the apex of the cone to the point where the lines from the plan intersect the base line of the cone.
5. Draw these lines on the end elevation. (Use dividers to take the vertical distance from the centre line in the plan to the diameter for each line and then mark it horizontally from the centre line of the end elevation on the base line, e.g. dimension 'A'.)
6. In the front elevation draw horizontal lines from the intersection of the cutting plane with the lines representing the divisions to the edge of the cone to give the true lengths.
7. Transfer these true lengths to the development. Draw in the curve plotted.
8. From the front elevation draw lines vertically down across the plan from the intersection of the sloping lines with the cutting plane. Where these cut the equivalent line in the plan is a point on the curve.
9. One set of points has to be obtained from the end elevation (i.e. 3,9). Measure the distance, using dividers, shown as 'C' and mark it on the plan. Draw in the curve plotted.
10. Draw lines horizontally across the end elevation from the intersection of the sloping lines with the cutting plane. Where they cut their equivalent lines is a point on the curve. Draw in the curve plotted.

Two cylinders of the same diameter intersecting at right angles

Both cylinders are 30 mm diameter. The vertical cylinder has a length of 70 mm and the horizontal cylinder has a length of 55 mm as shown in Fig. 6.13.

1. Draw the front elevation and plan of the intersecting cylinders. Divide both cylinders into 12 equal parts by using a semi-circle and number the divisions as in previous examples.
2. On both the front elevation and the plan draw lines from the divisions on the semi-circles across parts 'A' and 'B'. Where these lines intersect in the front elevation they form the curve of intersection of the two cylinders. Draw in the curve of intersection.
3. **Development of part 'B'**. As shown in the example on the development of a cylinder draw the full development of part 'B'. Mark on the 12 divisions and number them.
4. Using dividers take the distance for one of the divisions from the right-hand end of the cylinder to the point where it intersects with the curve in the front elevation and plot it on the equivalent line in the development (i.e. dimension 'Y'). Plot all points and draw in the curve.
5. **Development of part 'A'**. Repeat the procedure for drawing out the full development of part 'B' but ensure the height is 70 mm. Using dividers step off the distance from the base to the point of intersection for each division and mark it on the appropriate line (i.e. dimension 'X'). Draw in the curve.

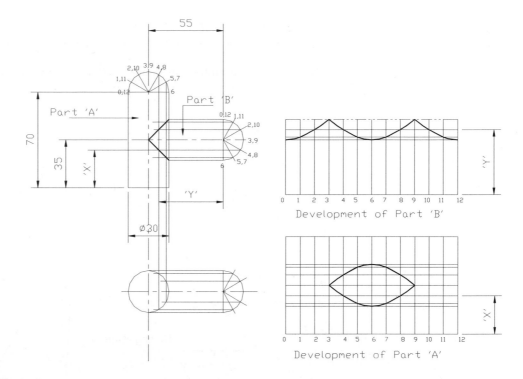

Fig. 6.13

Two cylinders of the same diameter intersecting at a given angle

The development of the two cylinders follows the same procedure as described above for two cylinders of the same diameter intersecting at right angles. The answers are shown in Fig. 6.14. Try this one on your own.

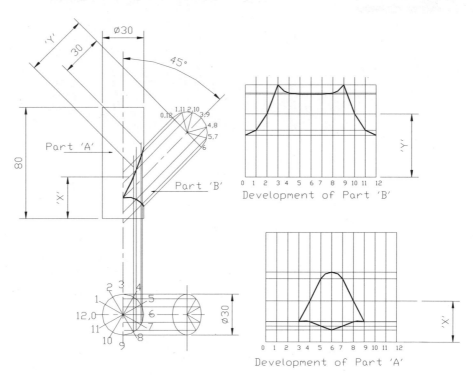

Fig. 6.14

Conic sections

This section is for information only. When a cone is cut by a plane the true shape can be a recognised curve. This is shown in Fig. 6.15.

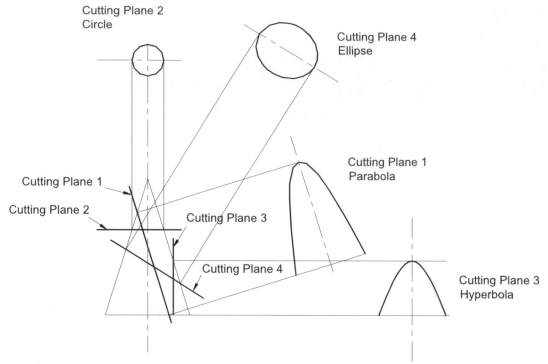

Fig. 6.15

Exercises Produce the development of each of the items shown in the drawings in Fig. 6.16.

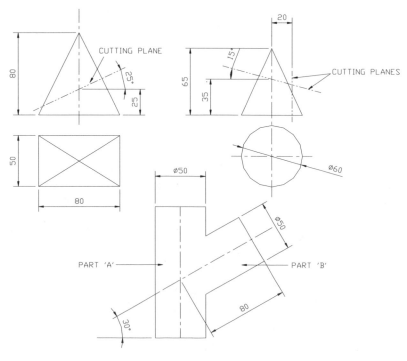

Fig. 16.6

Chapter 7

British Standards

The purpose of this chapter is to give the student a basic working knowledge of some of the British Standards used in the engineering drawing office. This is done by introducing the student to some of the basic points of BS 308 and other standards. In later chapters these standards will be applied and the student will be expected to conform to these.

Drawings are the link between the designer and the manufacturer of any article. To ensure that there is no confusion or ambiguity as to what is required it is essential that all involved should work to a common understanding or standard. In this country most companies use British Standards, and for engineering drawing this is BS 308 plus many other standards. This does not mean that they use these exclusively; many companies base their standards on British Standards but modify them in the light of satisfactory experience. If a company does use its own version of British Standards these should be committed to some form of publication so that everyone in the company, including subcontractors, have a clear understanding of what is included on the drawing.

Some standards that are referred to elsewhere in this book are those for drawing layout, type of projection, sections, dimensioning, tolerancing and geometric tolerancing.

Others that are of interest are as follows.

Line types

To help ensure that a drawing can be read quickly and accurately the lines used in a drawing must be recognised as serving a particular purpose. Those recommended by British Standards are shown in Fig. 7.1.

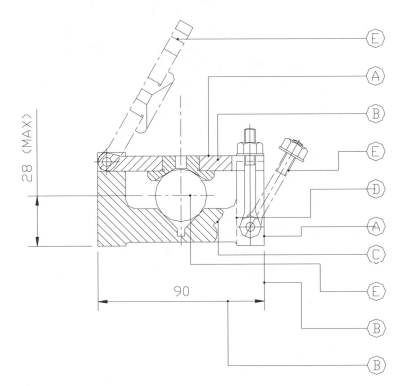

Fig. 7.1

- A – Continuous (thick): drawing outline and visible edges (0·7 mm thick).
- B – Continuous (thin): dimension lines, projection lines, hatching (0·35 mm thick).
- C – Continuous wavy (thick): limit of partial view (0·7 mm thick).
- D – Dashed (thin): hidden detail (0·35 mm thick).
- E – Long and short dash (thin): centre lines, phantom lines (0·35 mm thick).
- Not shown – Long and short dash (thick): centre lines indicating cutting planes (0·7 mm thick).

The use of two line thickness are recommended which should be in the ratio of 2:1 and should be from the range: 0·25, 0·35, 0·5, 0·7, 1·0, 1·4 and 2·0 mm. Those indicated in the list above are those generally used.

Lettering

A drawing should have lettering which is uniform and consistent in style. It may be upright or sloping but these should not be mixed. It should contain no unnecessary frills; also very fine lines may fail to reproduce well. The use of capital letters is preferred to lower case although lower case is acceptable when part of a standard abbreviation. British Standards recommend for A1, A2, A3 and A4 a minimum character height of 2·5 mm and for A0 3·5 mm. For A0, A1, A2 and A3 the drawing number should be a minimum of 7 mm.

Examples of acceptable styles are:

- A B C D E F G H I J K L M N O P Q R S T U V W X Y Z
  1 2 3 4 5 6 7 8 9 0 /
- a b c d e f g h i j k l m n o p q r s t u v w x y z
  1 2 3 4 5 6 7 8 9 0 /
- *A B C D E F G H I J K L M N O P Q R S T U V W X Y Z*
  1 2 3 4 5 6 7 8 9 0 /

Scales

A drawing should always state the scale used, although the drawing itself should never be scaled for manufacturing purposes. A drawing should be adequately dimensioned so that all sizes for manufacturing purposes are obtainable without any calculation. Some engineering companies add a warning on all drawings '**Do not scale**' or '**If in doubt ask**'.

The recommended scales are as follows:

- Full size: denoted as 1:1.
- Twice full size: denoted as 2:1.
- Five times full size: denoted as 5:1.
- Ten times full size: denoted as 10:1.

A drawing that is drawn at a scale greater than full size can be deceiving, therefore it is common practice, to aid appreciation of size, to add a view at actual size.

When making a drawing of large components and assemblies the component is drawn at a reduced size to fit the drawing sheet.

The recommended scales are as follows:

- Full size: denoted as 1:1.
- Half full size: denoted as 1:2.
- Fifth full size: denoted as 1:5.
- Tenth full size: denoted as 1:10.

Other common scales are 1:20, 1:50, 1:100, 1:200, 1:500 and 1:1000 etc.

It should be noted that when using computer-aided design and draughting all drawings are drawn full size. It is only at the production of a hard copy that scaling occurs.

Conventional representation of common features

Some features are drawn frequently and if drawn in full would take an unacceptable amount of time and would add to the confusion when large amounts of detail are involved. British Standards give recommendations for the drawing of many features which are less complex. Some of the most popular examples are shown in Fig. 7.2.

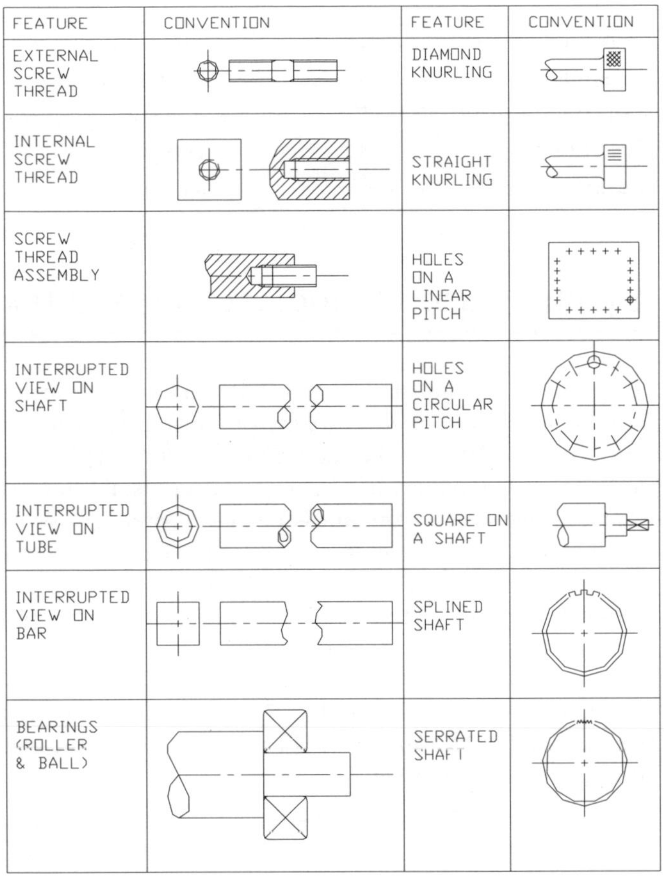

FEATURE	CONVENTION	FEATURE	CONVENTION
EXTERNAL SCREW THREAD		DIAMOND KNURLING	
INTERNAL SCREW THREAD		STRAIGHT KNURLING	
SCREW THREAD ASSEMBLY		HOLES ON A LINEAR PITCH	
INTERRUPTED VIEW ON SHAFT		HOLES ON A CIRCULAR PITCH	
INTERRUPTED VIEW ON TUBE		SQUARE ON A SHAFT	
INTERRUPTED VIEW ON BAR		SPLINED SHAFT	
BEARINGS (ROLLER & BALL)		SERRATED SHAFT	

Fig. 7.2

Abbreviations

To aid the production and reading of a drawing the words and phrases most often used are abbreviated. British Standards give the full list but Table 7.1 gives many of those most widely used.

Table 7.1   Widely used abbreviations

Word/phrase	Abbreviation	Word/phrase	Abbreviation
Across flats	A/F	Material	MATL
Assembly	ASSY	Maximum	MAX
Centres	CRS	Minimum	MIN
Centre line	CL or ℄	Number	NO
Chamfer	CHAM	Pattern number	PATT NO
Cheese head	CH HD	Pitch circle diameter	PCD
Countersink	CSINK	Radius	RAD or R
Counter bore	CBORE	Required	REQD

(continued)

Table 7.1   (*continued*)

Word/phrase	Abbreviation	Word/phrase	Abbreviation
Cylinder	CYL	Round head	RD HD
Diameter	DIA or $\varnothing$	Sheet	SHT
Drawing	DRG	Specification	SPEC
External	EXT	Spotface	SFACE
Figure	FIG	Square	SQ
Hexagon	HEX	Standard	STD
Internal	INT	Undercut	UCUT
Left hand	LH	Volume	VOL
Right hand	RH	Weight	WT
Long	LG	Maximum material condition	MMC

Symbols used to indicate surface texture

The quality of a finished surface has a direct relationship with the function, wear and cost of a component. The quality of the finished surface is a measure of its 'roughness' and can be related to the method of production. This relationship is very important and a British Standard has been produced as a guide (BS 1134). This standard gives a guide to the surface roughness produced by every process used in engineering. This means that a drawing may call for a surface roughness of a particular standard thus leaving the choice of production process to the manufacturing department. The required surface roughness for a particular feature is given on a drawing by a symbol and number, this number being a value in micrometres, microinches, or a roughness number.

The symbols are given in Fig. 7.3. These are combined with the surface roughness required either as a maximum or as a maximum and minimum reference. Examples of this are also given in Fig. 7.3.

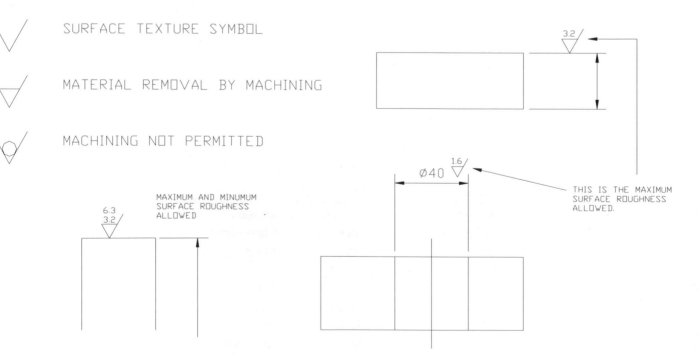

SURFACE TEXTURE SYMBOL

MATERIAL REMOVAL BY MACHINING

MACHINING NOT PERMITTED

3.2

6.3
3.2

MAXIMUM AND MINUMUM
SURFACE ROUGHNESS
ALLOWED

1.6
Ø40

THIS IS THE MAXIMUM
SURFACE ROUGHNESS
ALLOWED.

Fig. 7.3

Welding symbols

The joining of items by welding is a very technical process. The strength of the join required and the material thickness, etc., will dictate the method used. Therefore a welded joint will require some form of note attached to the weld. This is done by adding symbols to the drawing, a complete set of which can be found in BS 499 but a selection of which is given in Fig. 7.4. Examples of the application of welding symbols is given in Fig. 7.5.

FORM OF WELD	SYMBOL	ILLUSTRATION	FORM OF WELD	SYMBOL	ILLUSTRATION
CONVEX SINGLE V BUTT WELD			FLAT SINGLE VEE BUTT WELD		
CONVEX SQUARE BUTT WELD			DOUBLE U BUTT WELD		
CONVEX SINGLE U BUTT WELD			DOUBLE J BUTT WELD		
CONVEX SINGLE J BUTT WELD			SPOT WELD		
FILLET WELD			CONVEX DOUBLE V BUTT WELD		
SEALING RUN			STUD WELD		

Fig. 7.4

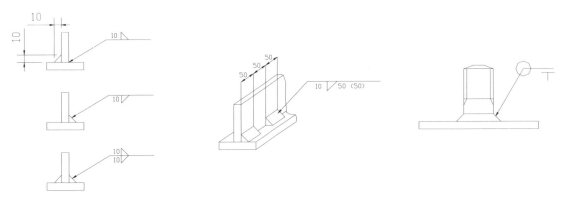

Fig. 7.5

A number of British Standards have been mentioned in this chapter. It expected that you will be required to refer to them at some time, but it is not recommended that you purchase any copies. The one you are most likely to refer to most is BS 308, this comes in four parts:

- Part 1: General principles.
- Part 2: Dimensioning and tolerancing.
- Part 3: Geometric tolerancing.
- Part 4: This includes a number of sections including a section on handling of computer based technical information.

The full version is very expensive, but most college and public libraries will have a copy. Students may obtain a copy of an abbreviated version (all sections in one volume) at a much reduced cost but the purchase of a copy, at this stage, is not recommended.

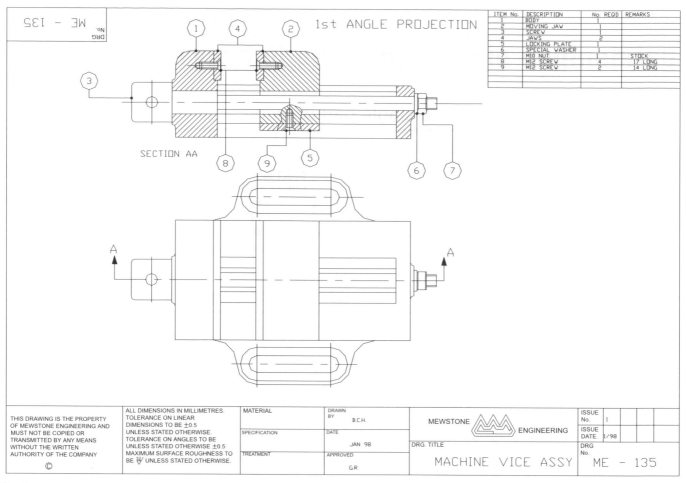

ITEM No.	DESCRIPTION	No. REQD	REMARKS
1	BODY	1	
2	MOVING JAW	1	
3	SCREW	1	
4	JAWS	2	
5	LOCKING PLATE	1	
6	SPECIAL WASHER	1	
7	M10 NUT	1	STOCK
8	M12 SCREW	4	17 LONG
9	M12 SCREW	2	14 LONG

1st ANGLE PROJECTION

SECTION AA

ALL DIMENSIONS IN MILLIMETRES. TOLERANCE ON LINEAR DIMENSIONS TO BE ±0.5 UNLESS STATED OTHERWISE. TOLERANCE ON ANGLES TO BE UNLESS STATED OTHERWISE ±0.5 MAXIMUM SURFACE ROUGHNESS TO BE ∜ UNLESS STATED OTHERWISE.	MATERIAL	DRAWN BY B.C.H.	MEWSTONE ENGINEERING		ISSUE No. 1	
	SPECIFICATION	DATE JAN 98			ISSUE DATE. 1/98	
	TREATMENT	APPROVED G.R.	DRG. TITLE MACHINE VICE ASSY	DRG No. ME – 135		

DRG No. ME – 135

Fig. 8.3

Combined detail and assembly drawing

This is used when it is convenient to show each item and the assembly on one drawing sheet. These are normally suitable for small articles in a one-off or limited batch situation. See Fig. 8.4.

Exploded drawing assembly

Generally this is a pictorial drawing showing all components in a three-dimensional form in their correct position for assembly. See Fig. 8.5. These drawings are invaluable in the do-it-yourself market such as car maintenance and kit assembly. They are also extremely useful in the stores, assisting in the location and ordering of components. This type of drawing also has the advantage of requiring less training in its understanding.

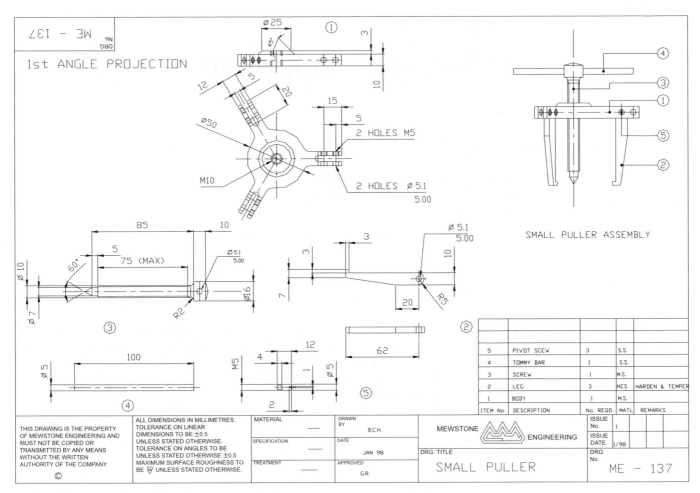

Fig. 8.4

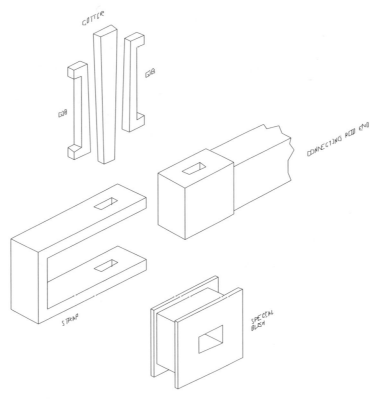

EXPERIMENTAL CONNECTING ROD ARRANGEMENT

Fig. 8.5

Chapter 9

Orthographic projection

The purpose of this chapter is to give the student knowledge, understanding and skill in the application of orthographic projection. This is done by:

- Introducing the origins of 1st and 3rd angle orthographic projection.
- The planes used and their names.
- Graded exercises.

To enable a component to be manufactured the ideas of the designer need to be accurately communicated to the manufacturer and the individual craftsmen who are going to make it. The most obvious way of doing this is by means of a picture or drawing. (Drawing is in fact a relatively modern method of communication, e.g. years ago very accurate models of ships were built first then the actual ship built from this model.)

Until recently it has been very difficult to produce drawings in three dimensions that could give all features accurately, with clarity and to scale. This led to the development of a system by which a three-dimensional object can be represented by a series of drawings (usually referred to as views or elevations) in two dimensions. This is called '**Orthographic projection**'.

In orthographic projection there are two methods, both having equal validity. These are known as **1st angle orthographic projection** and **3rd angle orthographic projection**. (These are usually shortened to 1st angle projection and 3rd angle projection). The names are derived from the method used to view the item being drawn.

In mathematics you will have met graphs and the nomenclature used to denote the quadrants. Figure 9.1(a) reminds you of these.

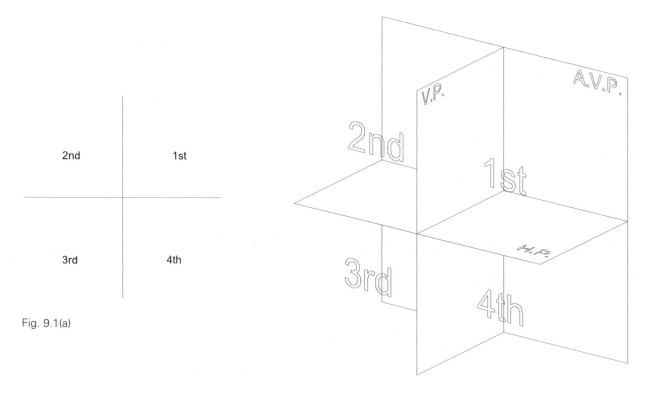

Fig. 9.1(a)

Fig. 9.1(b)

The line marked XY is called the horizontal plane (HP), where a plane is defined as a flat surface which has both length and breadth but no thickness. There are two other planes, both vertical planes. One is known as the vertical plane (VP) and the other as the auxiliary vertical plane (AVP). These can be seen clearly in Fig. 9.1(b). When an object is placed in the 1st quadrant it can be viewed in one of the three directions, indicated by the arrows labelled F, S and P as shown in Fig. 9.2. The face being viewed could be projected or drawn on one of the planes immediately behind and parallel to it. This is also shown in Fig 9.2.

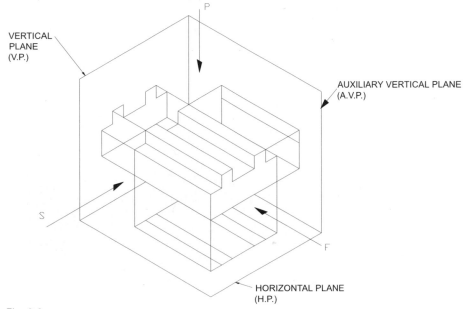

Fig. 9.2

When these planes are 'opened out' or laid flat we see three separate but related views of the object. See Fig. 9.3.

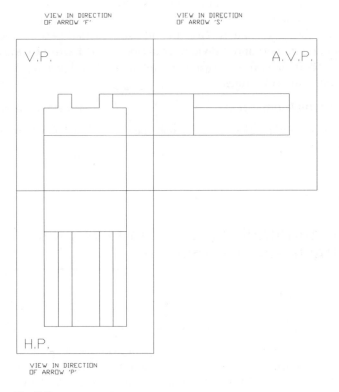

Fig. 9.3

All these views are in the 1st quadrant and therefore this type of projection is called **1st angle projection**.

Similarly when an object is placed in the 3rd quadrant we have the same views but they are not in the same positions. Figure 9.4(a) and (b) illustrate these points and as the views are in the 3rd quadrant this type of projection is called **3rd angle projection**.

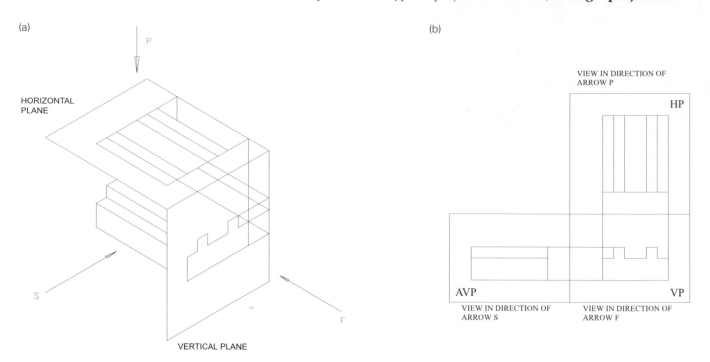

Fig. 9.4

As you can see the views themselves are identical but are found in different positions. This is a very brief description of the origins and reasons for the two different projection systems in use in engineering. It is important that you are able to see and recognise these systems quickly so that when presented with a drawing you are able to read and interpret it accurately. Note that for this illustration the same direction of viewing has been retained and the views could be called **front (F)**, **side (S)** and **plan (P)**.

To assist you in drawing and reading 1st and 3rd angle projection try using the following brief rules:

1st angle projection	*3rd angle projection*
The view from above is placed underneath.	The view from above is placed above.
The view from below is placed above.	The view from below is placed below.
The view from the left is placed on the right.	The view from the left is placed on the left.
The view from the right is placed on the left.	The view from the right is placed on the right.

Orthographic projection examples (by traditional method)

Example 1

The following instructions will take you through the basics.

1. Place an A3 sheet of drawing paper on the drawing and ensure that the top edge of the paper is set horizontal using the tee square and held down using tape or clips.
2. Measure in 10 mm at the mid-point of each side. Draw in the horizontal lines with the tee square and the vertical lines with the set square.

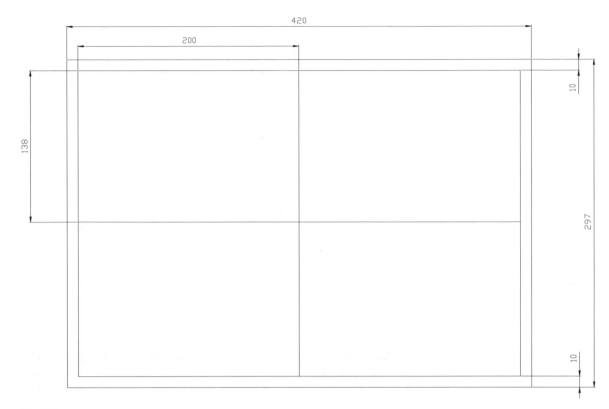

Fig. 9.5

3. Divide the area inside the border into four equal parts. This will allow the most economical use of the drawing sheet as well as giving some idea as to layout. See Fig. 9.5.
4. Using the amount of space correctly is always difficult when first beginning engineering drawing. The following instructions may be of some help in giving you space awareness. Using the top left quarter of the drawing sheet and assuming the item shown in Fig. 9.6 is to be drawn in 1st angle projection, measure the length and height of the drawing space available; you can check this by simple calculation.
5. You are required to produce three views (or elevations): a front view (or elevation), a side view (or elevation) and a plan, in 1st angle projection.

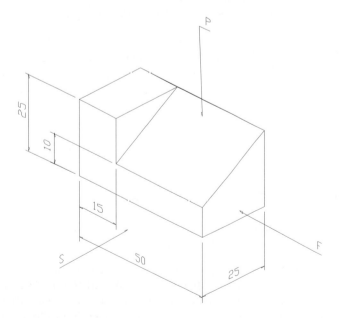

Fig. 9.6

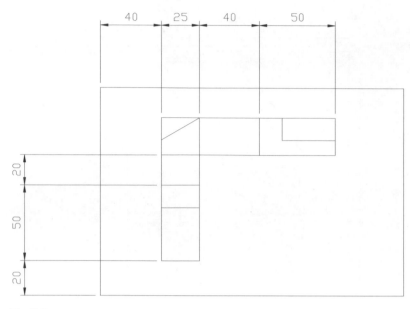

Fig. 9.7

Using a piece of scrap paper sketch out your answer and add the sizes to each side of the item being drawn. Using these dimensions determine approximately the space between each view assuming each space to be equal. Figure 9.7 illustrates what you should have.

Example of approximate spacing calculations:

Horizontal	Front view length	25 mm	
	Side view length	50 mm	
	Total	75 mm	
	Length available	200 mm	
	Three equal spaces are	200–75/3 = 41·6	
		= **40** approx.	

Vertical	Front view height	25 mm	
	Plan length height	50 mm	
	Total	75 mm	
	Height available	138 mm	
	Three equal spaces are	138–50/3 = 21	
		= **20** approx.	

6. Add faint lines to the space as indicated in Fig. 9.7. To position the view you must use the dimensions of the block, the spacing dimension are only approximate. For this simple item this has almost completed the drawing; just add faint lines to each view to show the portion removed.
7. Using a pencil with an HB lead darken in the lines that represent a hard edge. Note that you should try to obtain a line as dark as possible with a constant width that conforms to BS 308. Your answer should look similar to Fig. 9.7.

Example 2

You are required to produce three views: a front view, a side view and a plan, in 3rd angle projection of the object shown below in Fig. 9.8.

1. As in the first example it is suggested that you follow a similar method to lay out the views, but remember that the drawing must be in **3rd angle projection**. At this stage of learning engineering drawing it is suggested that you may find it good practice to sketch out your answer. If you do not feel confident with your answer discuss it with your lecturer before proceeding further.

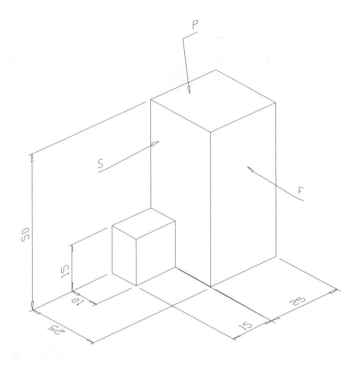

Fig. 9.8

2. Onto this sketch mark on the dimensions of each view and add the size of each of the spaces. (Note these can be approximate but your sizes for each view must be accurate.) It is suggested that the spacing between the views horizontally be approximately 45 and the spacing between the views vertically be approximately 20. (Ensure you confirm these figures.)
3. Using these sizes and the dimensions of the block set out your views correctly in one of the remaining quarters of the sheet.
4. Add the remaining lines required as faintly as possible.
5. When satisfied that the views are correct, using an HB pencil, darken all the lines that represent a hard edge. Your answer should look similar to Fig. 9.9.

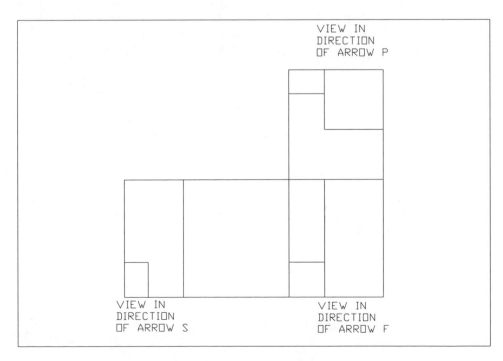

VIEW IN
DIRECTION
OF ARROW P

VIEW IN
DIRECTION
OF ARROW S

VIEW IN
DIRECTION
OF ARROW F

Fig. 9.9

Exercises Shown below in Fig. 9.10 are six items. In all drawings the front view is taken in the direction of arrow F, the side view is taken in direction of arrow S, and the plan view is taken in direction of arrow P. Items A, B and C are to be drawn in 1st angle projection, and items D, E and F are to be drawn in 3rd angle projection.

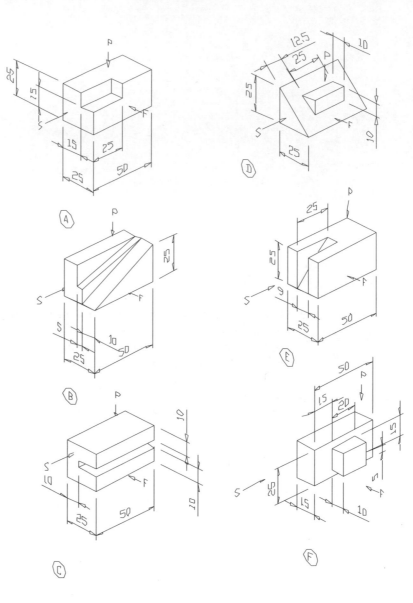

Fig. 9.10

Chapter 10

Pictorial projection

The purpose of this chapter is to give the student the skills and knowledge required to produce pictorial drawings of items that need to be seen in three dimensions. This is done by:

- Introducing isometric and oblique projection.
- Graded exercises in isometric projection.
- Graded exercises in oblique projection.

When a component is required to be seen in a three-dimensional form a method of pictorial projection can be used. There are a number of methods of pictorial projection but the two most commonly used in engineering are **isometric** and **oblique**. These methods of projection do not give an exact or true view of the component but they are an aid to design and industry in general particularly when information and instruction are to be given to non-technical and untrained people.

Isometric projection

In isometric projection all horizontal lines are drawn at 30° to the horizontal and all vertical lines are drawn vertical. Figure 10.1(a) shows the isometric axis. As this is a visual presentation of a component it would be sensible to use a simple exercise to show how to produce an isometric drawing.

The simple block shown in Fig. 10.1(b) is to be redrawn in isometric projection.

1. The first step is to draw the isometric axis using the 30°/60° set square.
2. Measure along all the lines 50 mm.
3. Draw in lines parallel to the axis as required from the points just measured.

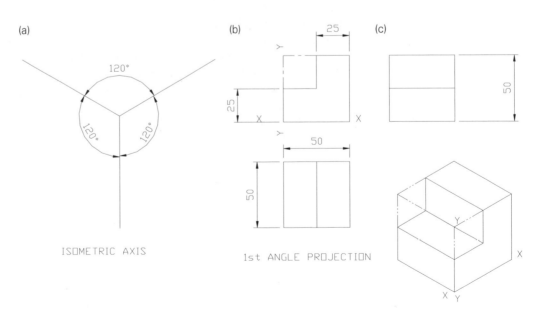

(a)   (b)   (c)

ISOMETRIC AXIS   1st ANGLE PROJECTION   ISOMETRIC PROJECTION

Fig. 10.1

This has produced the basic block. In this case we only have to remove a small portion to obtain a complete drawing, but this method of producing a working envelope should be used for all isometric drawings.

4. To complete the drawing mark on the vertical line and the relevant 30° lines the portion to be removed.
5. Darken the lines to show the true outline of the object as shown in Fig. 10.1(c).

To make the drawing look more realistic an isometric scale can be used. This is applied to all lines at 30°, but not to vertical lines. Figure 10.2(a) shows how such a scale can be constructed. The line at 45° has the true sizes marked along its length. These are then projected vertically down to the 30° line. All measurements are then taken using dividers from the 30° line. Figure 10.2(b) illustrates the difference.

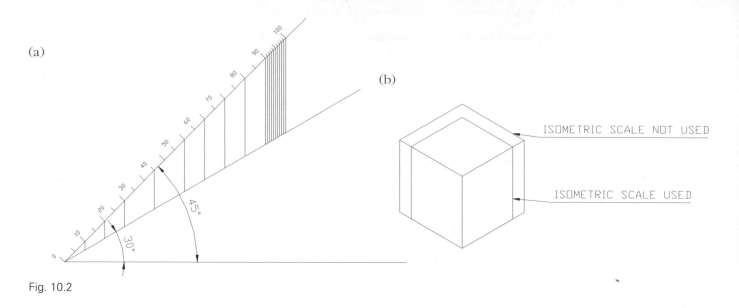

Fig. 10.2

Oblique projection

This appears to be a much easier projection to produce but it still needs care to produce a figure that will look correct.

It has the advantage that the most complex face can be drawn 'full on', i.e. the face with all the complex feature can be drawn as though it is facing you at right angles. The side faces are drawn at 45°. Figure 10.3 shows the same item as in Fig. 10.1 and then three versions of the block are produced to illustrate which face should be at the full on. To produce an item that looks authentic the lines at 45° are drawn to a length of half the true length.

1st ANGLE PROJECTION

OBLIQUE PROJECTION
(ALL MEASUREMENTS TO FULL SCALE)

OBLIQUE PROJECTION
(ALL MEASUREMENTS TO FULL SCALE)

OBLIQUE PROJECTION
RECEDING LINES DRAWN TO SCALE &
WITH THE MOST COMPLEX FEATURE
DRAWN FULL ON

Fig. 10.3

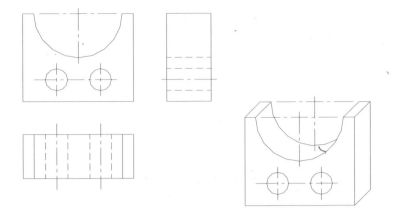

Fig. 10.4

Figure 10.4 gives an example of how the most complex face can be drawn using instruments and then given depth.

Exercises

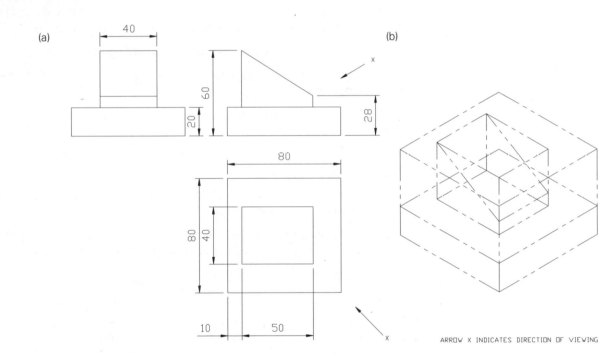

(a)

(b)

40

60

20

28

80

80

40

10   50

x

x

ARROW X INDICATES DIRECTION OF VIEWING

Fig. 10.5

Figure 10.5(a) shows a simple item drawn in 1st angle projection. The following is a brief outline of the steps that should be followed to produce an isometric view:

1 Draw the isometric axis required – the two lines at 30° and the vertical line.

2 Measure off the distances required along all lines.

3 Produce the box required to contain the item.

4 Produce lines to indicate the thickness of the base and a box to contain the portion on top of the base as shown in Fig. 10.5(b).

5 Produce the sloping face. Remember that this should slope towards the front so that it can be seen. Using a soft pencil draw in all visible outlines.

This method can also be used to produce isometric drawings freehand.

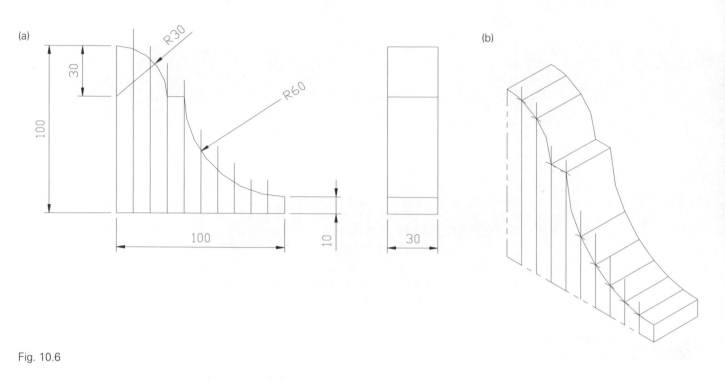

Fig. 10.6

Items containing curves can be time consuming to produce to give an accurate view. The item shown in Fig. 10.6(a) has two curves as well as a straight line.

1 Draw the shape of the face to be produced using orthographic projection.

2 Draw vertical construction lines across the face as shown in Fig. 10.6(a). These lines need not be equally spaced.

3 Draw the isometric box to contain the item. (This method can be used both with or without using the isometric scale.)

4 Draw on the isometric view vertical lines with their spacing as an accurate reflection of those in orthographic view.

5 Using dividers take the distance from the base to the point of intersection with the curve and step it off on the isometric view.

6 If you feel you need additional lines to obtain an accurate curve these may be added, but ensure that their position is accurately produced on the isometric view.

7 Draw in the curve as shown in Fig. 10.6(b).

It should be noted that the items shown in Fig. 10.7 could be in 1st angle or 3rd angle projection.

1 Produce an isometric view of the items shown in Fig. 10.7(a) to (c) with the point X as the lowest point in the foreground.

2. Produce oblique views of the items shown in Fig. 10.7(d) to (e).

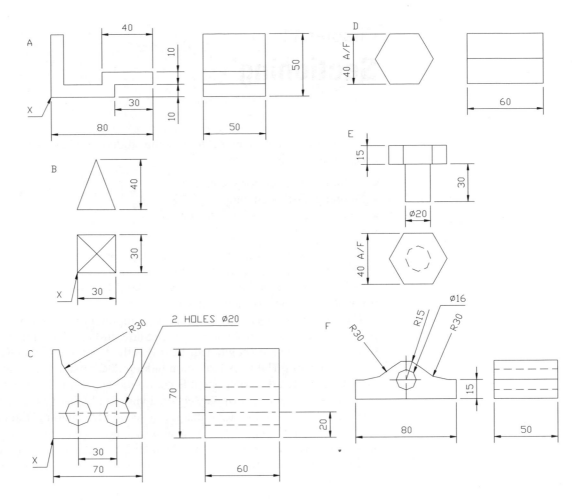

Fig. 10.7

Chapter 11

Sectioning

The purpose of this chapter is to give the student the knowledge and understanding of sectioning. This is done by:

- Defining the need for sectioning.
- Defining basic sectioning.
- Illustrating more complex sectioning.
- Graded exercises.

A section is drawn to show the hidden shape or form. The shape or form may be hidden due to it being part of the inside of the component or it may be hidden by a larger area no matter where the view is taken. This will help to clarify what would normally be shown as hidden detail.

   The section is obtained by cutting the component into two parts at some convenient point, in many cases this will be a centre line. In Fig. 11.1 a number of views of the same component are shown, Fig. 11.1(a) is the front and end elevation drawn in 3rd angle projection. The lines indicating hidden detail make the view seem more complex than it really is. If the component is cut on the line AA in the front elevation and viewed in the direction of the arrows a sectional view is obtained as shown in Fig. 11.1(b). The sectional view should indicate that it is a section by 'shading' the cut surface with evenly spaced lines at 45° called 'hatching' and by a note adjacent to the view stating where the section is taken, in this case Section AA. Hidden detail should not be shown on a section as this could make the section itself confusing and negate the reason for taking the section.

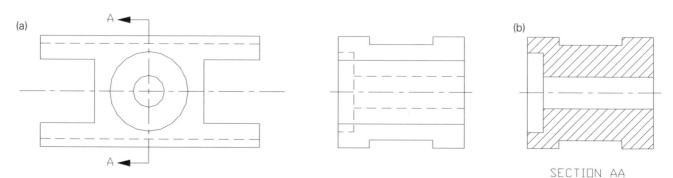

Fig. 11.1

SECTION AA

   When a section is taken through two or more items forming an assembly each item should be hatched at alternate angles. It may be necessary to change the spacing. Figure 11.2 shows a section through a small assembly.

   Although there are many variations that can only be understood with time and practice, Fig. 11.2 illustrates many of the most common. The following notes refer to the balloon references in Fig. 11.2:

1. A half section – used when a component is symmetrical; one view shows both the inside and outside.
2. Nuts, bolts and washers etc. – these are not sectioned when cut longitudinally.
3. & 4. Various items are not sectioned such as shafts, keys etc.
5. Wheel spokes are not sectioned/cut when taken longitudinally.
6. Revolved section used to show the cross-sectional shape of the spoke.
7. Threads to be shown as given in the conventional representation of common features.
8. Sections must be referenced or 'called up' to give additional indication as to where they are taken.

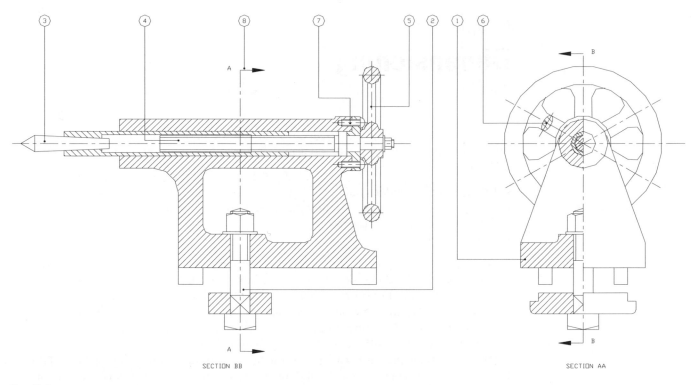

SECTION BB

SECTION AA

Fig. 11.2

| **Exercises** | **1** Draw a half section through the 'special pulley' shown in Fig. 11.3 (1). |
| | **2** Produce a section on the centre line AA for the item shown in Fig. 11.3 (2). |

1

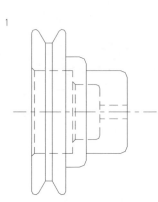

2

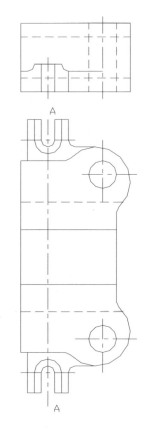

Fig. 11.3

Chapter 12

Dimensioning

The purpose of this chapter is to give the student the basic knowledge and understanding required to read and apply dimensions to engineering drawings. This is done by:

- Briefly defining dimensioning.
- Giving some basic rules as to how dimensions should be applied.
- Defining the types of dimensions.
- Graded exercises.

A drawing should provide a complete set of working instructions for the manufacture of the component. The dimensions define the geometric characteristics such as length, diameters, angles and positions. Each dimension which defines a characteristic should appear on the drawing only once. If all dimensions are included correctly the manufacturer should not find it necessary to scale the drawing or perform any mathematics to obtain a dimension for any feature of the component.

Dimensions fall into three categories, functional, non-functional and auxiliary. From Fig. 12.1 you will see that functional dimensions are those which control the way in which the component works. Non-functional dimensions are those which do not affect the way in which the component works, but they may affect its efficiency. Auxiliary dimensions are an aid to the manufacture of the component in that they may give such things as an overall length and thus eliminate any error that may occur on the shop floor.

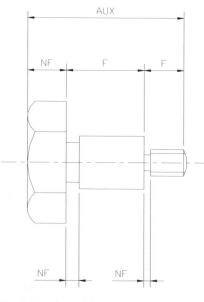

Fig. 12.1

Functional dimensions should be from a datum. Datums on one component should coincide with datums on other components when assembled. These may be centre lines or faces.

When dimensioning a drawing the following points should be applied (refer to Fig. 12.2):

1. Projection and dimension lines are thin continuous lines 0·3 mm thick.
2. Where possible all dimensions should be placed outside the outline of the drawing to ensure that maximum clarity is maintained.

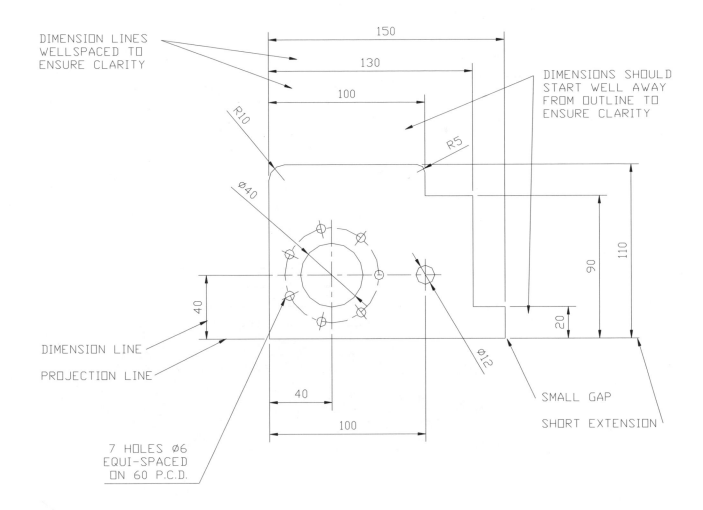

DIMENSION LINES
WELLSPACED TO
ENSURE CLARITY

150

130

100

DIMENSIONS SHOULD
START WELL AWAY
FROM OUTLINE TO
ENSURE CLARITY

R10

R5

Ø40

110

90

20

DIMENSION LINE

PROJECTION LINE

Ø12

40

SMALL GAP

SHORT EXTENSION

40

100

7 HOLES Ø6
EQUI-SPACED
ON 60 P.C.D.

Fig. 12.2

3. The projections lincs should start 3 mm from the drawing. This gives emphasis to the drawing shape.
4. Dimensions should not be cramped. It is recommended that dimensions are spaced 10–12 mm apart with a much larger gap between the drawing and the first dimension. The smaller dimensions should be closest to the drawing and the larger ones farthest away. This will avoid the crossing of projection and dimension lines unnecessarily.
5. The arrow heads should be uniform in size and about 3–4 mm long and 2 mm thick. They must **touch** the projection line.
6. Centre lines should never be used as dimension lines. (They may be substituted for projection lines in appropriate circumstances.)
7. To assist the reading of dimensions all figures and notes should be placed so that they can be read when the drawing has its bottom closest to the reader or when the drawing has been rotated clockwise from the right-hand side through a right angle. (Some dimensions and notes may be at a different angle due to dimension alignment but should be able to be read from the right-hand side.)
8. Avoid long leader lines for such features as holes and radii. It is better to repeat these dimensions.
9. Dimensions should be in millimetres (mm not cm). When a whole number is given it should be given without the decimal point, e.g. 30 not 30·0. If a dimension is less than 1 it should be written as 0·4 not as ·4 – the decimal point could be lost on a drawing in the workshop.
10. All dimensions should be made from a feature which is a datum, e.g. a surface or a centre line.

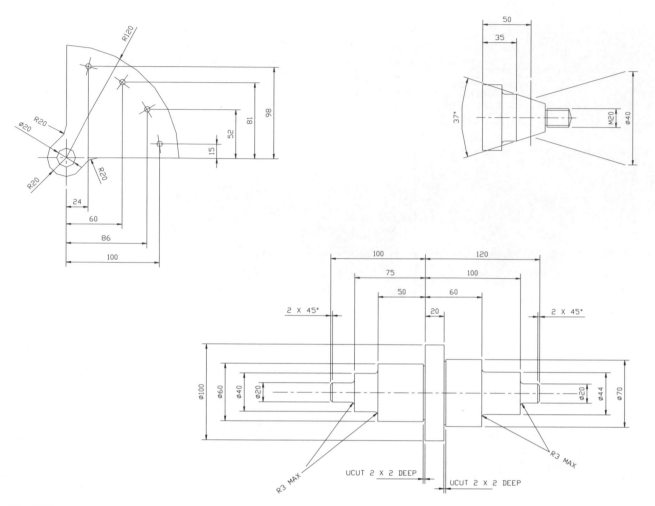

Fig. 12.3

Figure 12.3 illustrates how datums may be used for dimensioning. It also illustrates how an angle may be dimensioned using a datum. It should be noted that this datum must have a coincident datum on the mating item.

Exercises

1 & 2 Redraw either freehand or using a drawing board and add all dimensions needed to manufacture the items. You will need to determine a datum in both cases.

3 & 4 Redraw both items using dimensions agreed with your lecturer. Determine a datum and add all dimensions that will be required for manufacture.

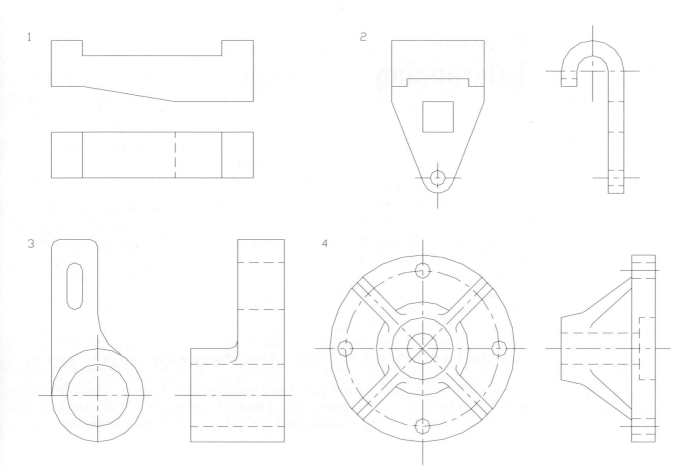

Fig. 12.4

Chapter 13

Tolerancing

- The purpose of this chapter is to give the student the knowledge and understanding required to read and apply tolerances. This is done by:

- Briefly investigating interchangeability.
- Briefly studying BS 4500.
- Applying tolerances through graded exercises.

To ensure that an assembly will function correctly the component parts must fit together in a predetermined manner. This difficulty is added to by the fact that no component can be manufactured to an exact size. Therefore a designer has to make the decision as to what are the extremes of size that are acceptable for each functional dimension to ensure satisfactory operation in service. The designer must also consider the costs of manufacture; if the extremes of size are very close together then the cost to manufacture will be high. The determination of the extremes of size are part of a topic known as **limits and fits** which is part of the subject of **interchangeability**. This topic is covered in depth in another unit.

In this unit we are only concerned as to how the tolerance is to be shown on the drawing in a clear and concise manner, but to do this it is necessary to look briefly at the whole system. Figure 13.1 illustrates the basic elements of an **interchangeable system**.

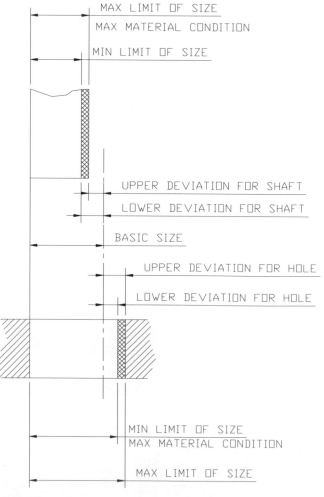

Fig. 13.1

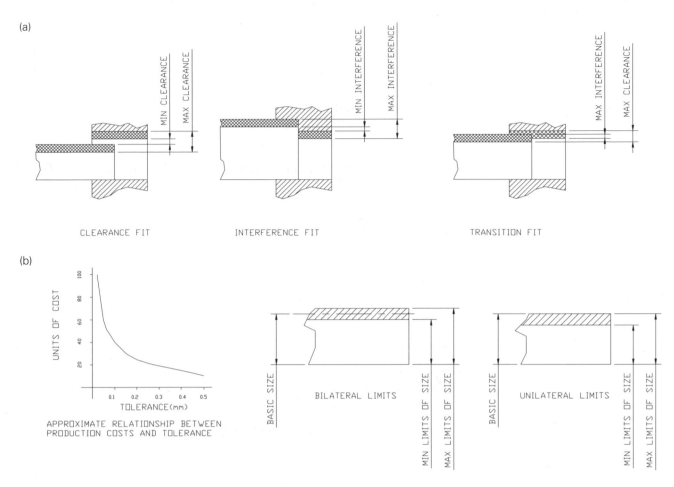

Fig. 13.2

The three basic types of fit obtainable are illustrated in Fig. 13.2(a). Figure 13.2(b) shows what is meant by 'bilateral and unilateral limits'; it should be noted that in unilateral limits the tolerance may be added to or subtracted from the basic size.

As a guide to costs a graph showing the approximate relationship between tolerance and production has also been included. This is to emphasise the need for care when specifying tolerance.

There are two recommended bases of fit: hole basis and shaft basis. In the hole basis the hole is the constant size (i.e. if the hole diameter is 10 mm there will be a small tolerance for manufacturing purposes and the shaft is varied to obtain the fit required). This means that the hole could be manufactured relatively easily and in the smaller range of sizes it may be possible to use a reamer.

Examples

The following illustrate how limits are determined using BS 4500A given the nominal size and the tolerance combination to be applied.

Nominal size 12 mm, hole/shaft tolerance combination H8/f7

From BS 4500A the following can be found:

$$
\begin{array}{ll}
H\,8 & f\,7 \\
+27 & -16 \\
0 & -34
\end{array}
$$

It should be noted that these numbers are in thousandths of a millimetre (i.e. 0·001 mm).

Limits	*Hole*	*Shaft*
Max.	12·027	11·984
Min.	12·000	11·966
Max. conditions	12·000	11·984

Max. clearance	0·061
Min. clearance	0·016

Nominal size 118 mm, hole/shaft tolerance combination H7/p6

From BS 4500A

H 7	*p 6*
+35	+59
0	+37

Limits	*Hole*	*Shaft*
Max.	118·035	118·059
Min.	118·000	118·037
Max. conditions	118·000	118·059

Max. interference	0·059
Min. interference	0·002

Nominal size 38 mm, hole/shaft tolerance combination H7/n6

From BS 4500A

H 7	*n 6*
+25	+33
0	+17

Limits	*Hole*	*Shaft*
Max.	38·025	38·033
Min.	38·000	38·017
Max. conditions	38·000	38·033

As this is a transition fit, an interference or clearance fit could be obtained:

Max. interference	0·033
Max. clearance	0·008

Below Fig. 13.3 illustrates how tolerance may be shown on a drawing. Note that in many companies the maximum material condition is always given as the number at the top of the limits.

Exercises

Using BS 4500A determine:

1 The type of fit between the mating parts.

2 The MMC of each part.

3 Maximum and minimum interference or clearance.

Nominal size	*Hole/shaft combination*
50	H7/h6
10	H7/n6
12	H8/f7
15	H7/p6

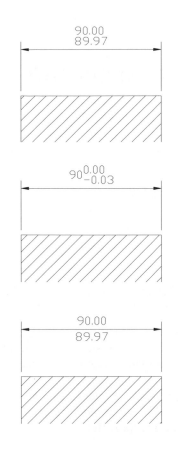
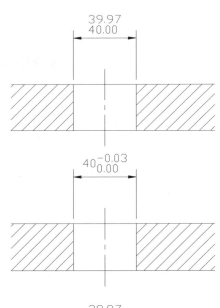
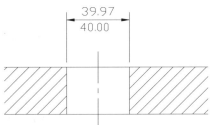

Fig. 13.3

Chapter 14

Geometrical tolerancing

The purpose of this chapter is to introduce the student to geometrical tolerancing. It will give the student basic knowledge and skills in the interpretation and application of geometrical tolerances by:

- Outlining when geometrical tolerances are required.
- Illustrating the symbols used.
- Illustrating the methods of application.
- Giving examples.
- Graded exercises.

Reasons for applying geometrical tolerance

Geometrical tolerances are used to control more precisely the shape and form of a component. They are only used when the shape or form has a particular function and errors would result in poor performance. Geometrical tolerances are applied in *addition* to dimensional tolerances.

Before the introduction of geometrical tolerancing most drawings which required the control of shape and form would have simple instructions printed against the required feature, e.g. '**surface to be flat and parallel**'. It will be appreciated that this expression leaves itself open to many interpretations.

The two extreme interpretations of this expression may be that the shape or form:

- Is not within the tolerances desired and the component will not perform to the standards required.
- Is produced using very small tolerances that are extremely expensive to manufacture.

Interpretation of the designers requirements is critical and any errors could be expensive, but the use of symbols which have a fairly precise meaning has illuminated many of the misunderstandings.

Symbols

Table 14.1   Table of geometrical tolerance symbols

Tolerance characteristics	Symbol	Application
Form tolerances		
Straightness	⎯	A straight line. The edge or axis of a feature.
Flatness	▱	A plane surface.
Roundness	○	The periphery of a circle. Cross-section of a bore, cylinder, cone or sphere.
Cylindricity	⌭	The combination of roundness, straightness, and parallelism of cylindrical surfaces.
Profile of a line	⌒	The theoretical form of a profile defined by true boxed dimensions.
Profile of a surface	⌓	The theoretical form of a surface defined by true boxed dimensions
Attitude tolerances		
Parallelism	//	Parallelism of a feature related to a datum.
Squareness	⊥	Surfaces, axes or lines positioned at right angles to each other.
Angularity	∠	The angular displacement of surfaces, axes or lines from a datum.

(continued)

Table 14.1   (*continued*)

Tolerance characteristics	Symbol	Application
Composite tolerances		
Runout		The position of a fixed point on a surface of a part which is rotated 360° about its axis.
Location tolerances		
Position	⊕	The deviation of a feature from a true position.
Concentricity	◎	The relationship between two cylinders or circles having a common axis.
Symmetry	☰	The symmetrical position of a feature related to a datum.

The symbols used to control the geometrical shape and form of a component are themselves simple but their application needs to be considered very carefully. The application of a geometrical tolerance symbol to control a feature or shape may affect control of another, e.g. positional tolerance may also control squareness and straightness.

The examples that follow will help guide the student through this complex topic, but it should be appreciated that only continued practice will give the knowledge that is required to apply geometrical tolerances with confidence. The application of a geometrical tolerance should not imply any particular method of manufacture.

Methods of application

Geometric tolerances are indicated by giving the following information in a frame:

- The characteristic symbol for the feature and related feature.
- The tolerance value.
- The letter identifying the datum when specified.

Examples

Symbol for tolerance characteristic ——→ ◎ | ⌀ 0.05 | A ——— Datum identification letter

↑
Total tolerance

Fig. 14.1

The frame in Fig. 14.1 has to be shown referring to the toleranced feature:

- Surface or plane.
- Axis or plane.

See Fig. 14.2.

Fig. 14.2

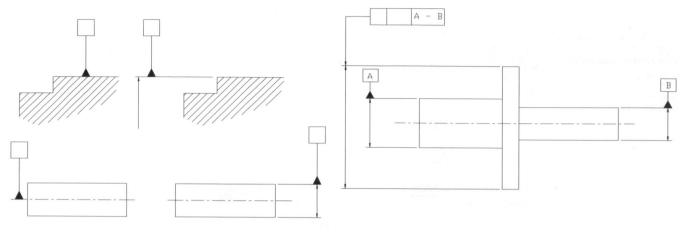

Fig. 14.3

Figure 14.3 illustrates specifying the datum, showing single datum and multiple datums.

Examples of the application of geometrical tolerances are shown in Figs. 14.4–14.6.

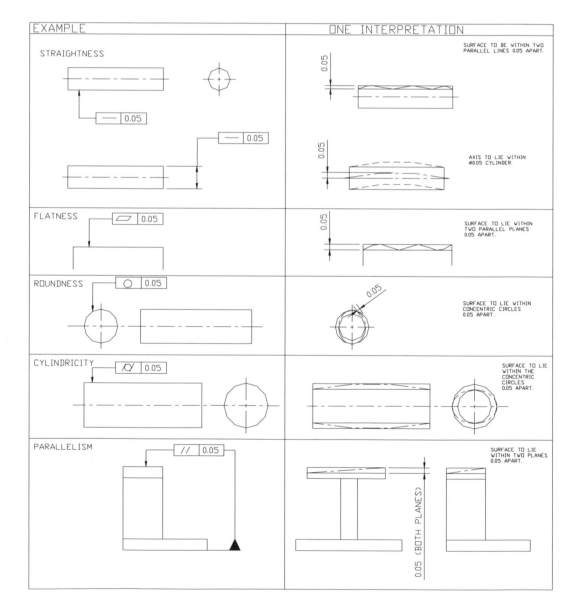

Fig. 14.4

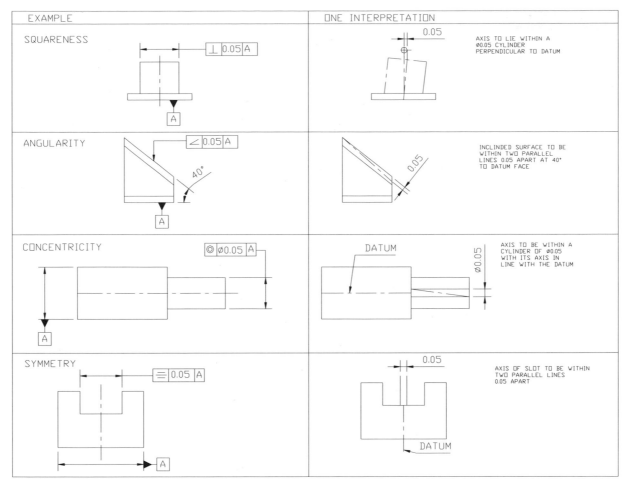

Fig. 14.5

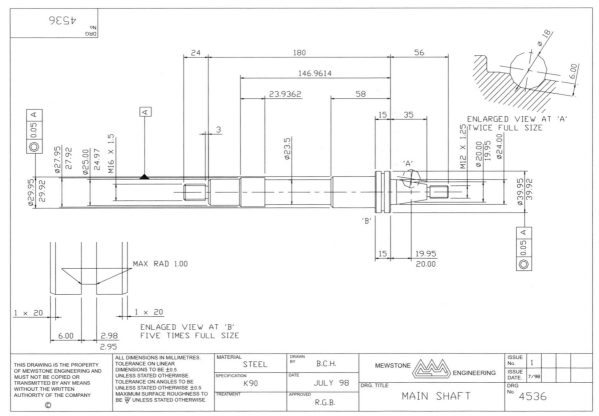

Fig. 14.6

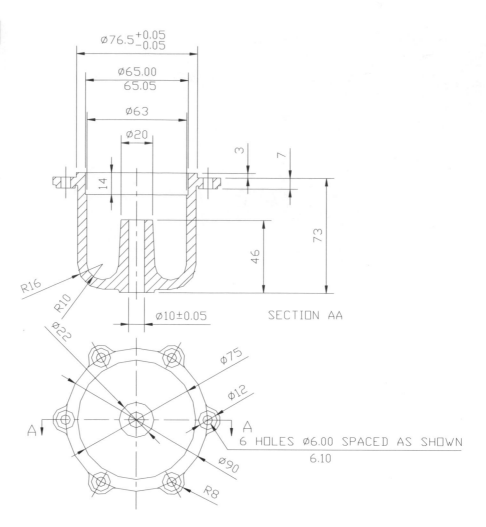

Fig. 14.7

Redraw the component shown in Fig. 14.7.

1 Fully dimension, but do not copy the layout used; you are expected to improve the method of application.

2 Add geometrical tolerances to ensure:
   ● The horizontal datum is at right angles to the centre line.
   ● The 10 mm diameter hole is concentric within 0·05 of the 65 mm diameter.
   ● The location diameter 76·5 mm is to be concentric within 0·05 mm to the 65 mm diameter.
   ● The six holes 6 mm diameter are to be within 0·05 within the given position.
   Note: All dimensions not given are at the discretion of the student.

Chapter 15

Circuit diagrams

The purpose of this chapter is to introduce the student to symbols used to produce electrical and electronic circuit diagrams and pneumatic and hydraulic circuit diagrams. This is done by introducing the student to the British Standards for the symbols and giving illustrations and exercises for some circuit diagrams. It should be noted that it is not intended to go into the theory of building up circuits, only the production of the circuit diagrams, therefore this chapter should be used in conjunction with theory taught in electrical and electronics and pneumatics and hydraulics.

There are many symbols covered by British Standards, but in this chapter we shall only concern ourselves with two sets. These are the symbols for:

- Electrical and electronic equipment and circuits (BS 3939).
- Pneumatic and hydraulic equipment and circuits (BS 2917).

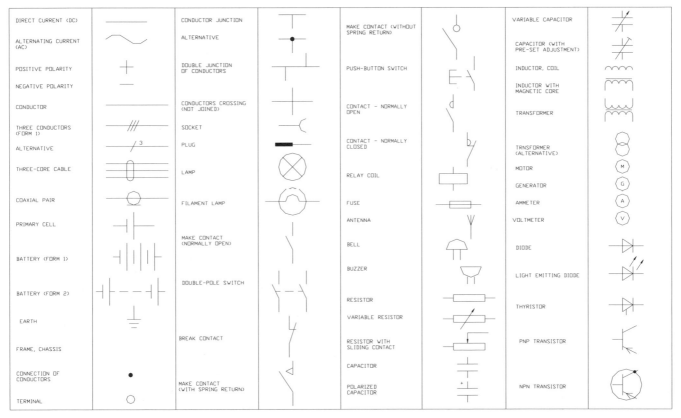

Fig. 15.1

Some selected symbols are shown in Fig. 15.1 (electrical and electronic symbols) and Fig. 15.2 (pneumatic and hydraulic symbols) the full versions of which can be found in British Standards. Producing the symbols so that they conform to British Standards or the standards used by the company will be time consuming. When a circuit is being designed or modified it adds an interest factor and relieves some of the feelings of time wasting but it can be very frustrating when a small number of symbols have to be repeated many times. To speed up the drawing of the symbols and to enhance their accuracy and appearance to the standards adopted there are plastic templates produced for both sets of symbols being discussed. These give a standard size and shape. Some companies, particularly in the pneumatics and hydraulics field, who produce the equipment, also have templates available.

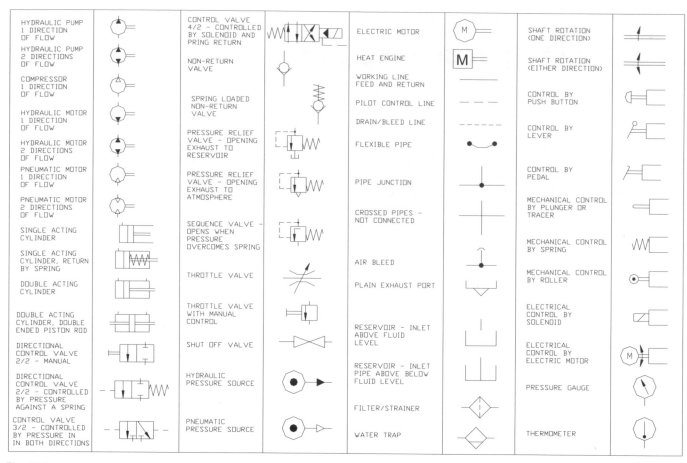

Fig. 15.2

This is an area that has seen the introduction of the computer to save time in the design and drawing of the circuit. There are programs available in the electronics field that will allow a designer to produce a circuit and the computer program will make most of the connections as well as test the end result. There are similar pneumatics and hydraulics software available. In both cases the ability to test the result before build and the ability to modify quickly have made them invaluable tools.

If it is a one-off situation and no testing is involved almost any CAD system can be used to produce circuit diagrams. This would entail producing each symbol and storing it in a library and recalling them from memory as required and adding them to the circuit being produced. This does not have the facility for testing the circuits and, if only used infrequently, the production of a library of symbols could be a waste of time.

Exercises

1 Figure 15.3 shows three circuits or parts of circuits with each item numbered. Identify each item for the given circuits. Redraw one of the circuits using traditional means. The use of a template is acceptable.

2 Figure 15.4 shows two diagrams of hydraulic/pneumatic circuits. In the top diagram identify the symbols that are numbered 1 to 9. The second diagram shows a layout for a circuit. Redraw this using symbols only.

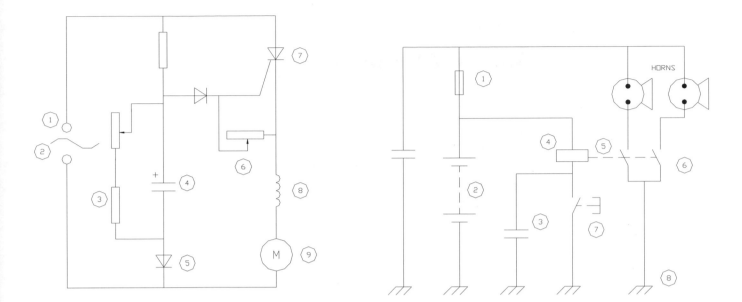

Fig. 15.3

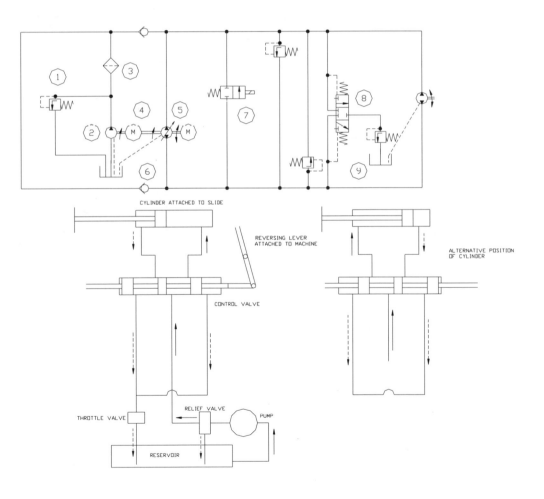

Fig. 15.4

Chapter 16

Auxiliary views

The purpose of this chapter is to give the student the knowledge, understanding and some skill in the use of auxiliary views.

This is done by giving:

- A simple example of the reasons for the use of auxiliary views.
- Worked examples.
- Graded exercises.

When a component has its principal faces parallel to one of the three main planes it can be adequately represented by the normal views. However, many components have a face or faces that are not parallel to any of the principal planes so that when viewed from the normal directions they do not give the true shape and in some cases they are confusing. This can be overcome by using an auxiliary view or views. These auxiliary views enable the true shape to be used to give dimensions and any additional information without creating confusion.

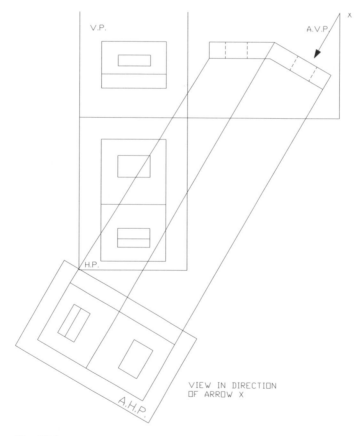

VIEW IN DIRECTION OF ARROW X

Fig. 16.1

In Fig. 16.1 a component is shown with two holes. The true shape of the one hole is shown in the plan view, but the true shape of the hole in the sloping face cannot be seen in any of the views. A true shape can only been seen if a view is taken at right angles to the sloping face as shown in Fig. 16.1.

This additional or auxiliary view is drawn at a convenient position in the projection being used (i.e. 1st or 3rd angle projection) as shown in Fig. 16.1.

In Fig. 16.1 the auxiliary view is projected from the end view; therefore the resulting view is an auxiliary plan.

Example 1

(a)   (b)

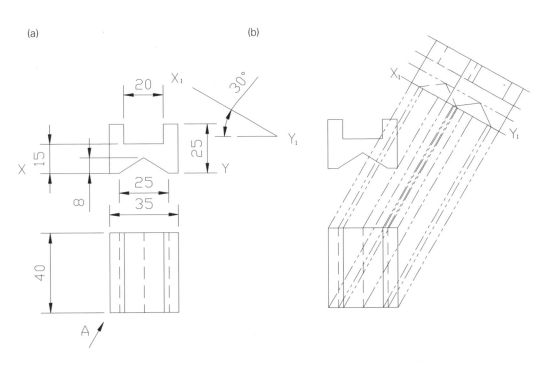

Fig. 16.2

1. Copy the drawing shown in Fig. 16.2(a). Ensure that the line marked X_1Y_1 is included at 30° and that it is clear of the drawing as this is to form the base of the auxiliary view.
2. Using lines of construction quality draw lines from each of the corners in the plan view at 60° through the line X_1Y_1 as shown in Fig. 16.2(b).
3. Mark off on the lines the height of the component from the front view above the X_1Y_1 line. This should produce a line parallel to the X_1Y_1 line at a distance above of 25 mm.
4. Draw lines from each of the corners of the rectangular channel at 60° through the X_1Y_1 line.
5. Mark off the distance of 15 mm to give the depth of the channel and draw a line through them. Again this should be parallel to the X_1Y_1 line.
6. You are viewing the component at 60° from the bottom left-hand corner in the plan. Therefore the rectangular channel (and the vee channel) can be seen.
7. Draw lines at 60° from the plan up through the X_1Y_1 line from all corners and the bottom of the vee.
8. Mark off a line 8 mm above the X_1Y_1 line to give the depth of the vee.
9. This completes the construction but care must be taken when darkening the correct lines – see Fig. 16.2(b). This is an **auxiliary elevation**.

Example 2

1. Copy the drawing shown in Fig. 16.3(a) including the line XY and the line X_1Y_1 at 30°.
2. Draw lines at 60° down through the X_1Y_1 line from each corner of the base (top and bottom) and the apex of the pyramid.
3. Measure the distance from the XY line to the apex of the pyramid in the plan using divider and step this distance off along the line extending from the apex from the X_1Y_1 line. This is shown as the distance 'A'. Repeat this for the base top and bottom.
4. The construction is completed. Darken in the lines to give the shape; refer to the drawing shown in Fig. 16.3(b). This is an **auxiliary plan**.

(a)

(b)

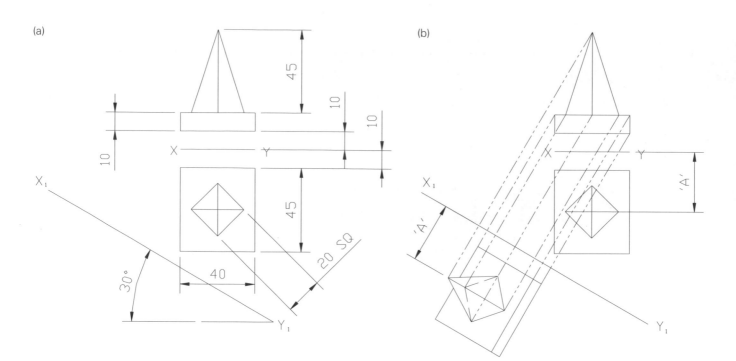

Fig. 16.3

Make an auxiliary view for each of the drawings shown in Fig. 16.4.

- In A an auxiliary plan is required on the line XY.
- In B an auxiliary elevation is required on the line XY.
- In C an auxiliary elevation is required on the line XY.
- In D an auxiliary elevation is required on the line XY.

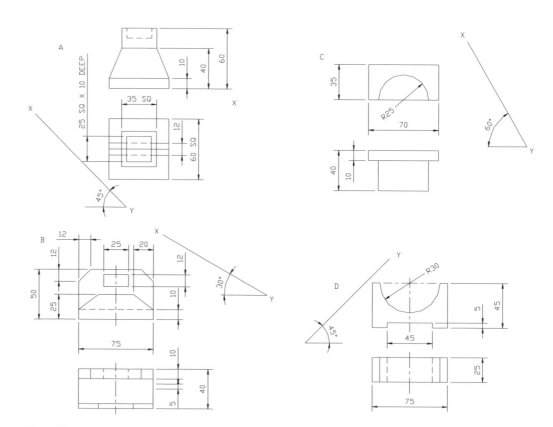

Fig. 16.4

Chapter 17

CAD/CAM

The purpose of this chapter is to introduce CAD/CAM to the student by looking at the following:

- The hardware and software requirements.
- The operating systems used.
- The inputs required and the outputs obtained.

Computers are widely used throughout engineering and manufacturing in general. Their application assists all aspects of the companies' operations; these include the technical departments, financial departments and the general organisational areas. In engineering computers are being used in the following areas:

- Computer-aided design and draughting (CADD) or (CAD)
- Computer numerical control (computer controlled machine tools) (CNC)
- Computerised material handling (robotics)
- Computer-aided quality control (CAQC)
- Computer-aided production control and management (CAPM)
- Computer-integrated manufacture (CIM)

These names and acronyms mean very little and hide a complex area of computer-assisted work. A brief overview of each area will help put the computer and its impact on engineering into perspective.

- **CAD**
  The purpose of CAD is to produce the necessary design and detail drawings for the manufacture of a product.
- **CNC**
  Machine tools that are computer controlled can receive suitably modified information from a CAD system to control the cutting tool path and thus produce all machined components.
- **Robots**
  These can be designed and programmed to handle the materials before, during and after the machining processes. They can also work under conditions that would be harmful to human beings such as spray painting.
- **Quality Control**
  Data produced by a CAD system can be used in the quality control system to monitor and control the products being produced.
- **CAPM**
  This is the tool which aids the management of the manufacturing and production processes. In general terms it allows the whole production and manufacturing system to be managed.
- **CIM**
  This usually refers to the total integration of the production and manufacturing system including cost control and ordering and marketing as well as design and machining. The main elements of a CAD/CAM system are shown in Fig. 17.1.

Before going into the CAD System it will be advantageous to understand what is understood by the acronym CAD or CADD. Generally it is accepted that CAD means **computer-aided design** and the alternative CADD means **computer-aided design and draughting**. In this section we shall use the acronym CAD to cover both draughting and design.

In its broadest sense CAD refers to the application of a computer system to aid the solution of a design problem. It is a technique in which the engineer or designer and the Computer work together using the best characteristics of each. Before studying the subject in greater depth it must be stated that the computer is no substitute for the good

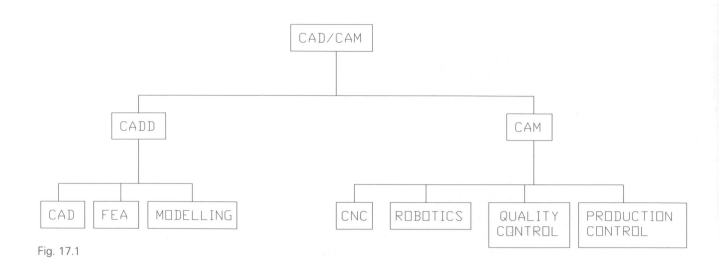

Fig. 17.1

designer. Remember '**Rubbish In Rubbish Out**'. (If inaccurate information is put into the computer you will not get accurate information from the computer.)

As with all types of computer systems the designer will communicate with the system through various components such as the keyboard, mouse, screen (VDU), tablet and plotter. The designer may pose questions and receive answers within a very short time. This is particularly noticeable when complex repetitive calculations are required. The computer will produce results that are both accurate and reliable (assuming the information given to the computer is accurate and reliable). The designer can test ideas and see the different effects very quickly. These can be repeated till a satisfactory solution is obtained.

The designer, today, has access to substantial computing power which can be used to improve design accuracy; this can shorten the design process thus making the time from concept to manufacture much shorter.

Typical capabilities of a CAD system may include the production of:

- Design layouts.
- Detail drawings in 1st or 3rd angle projection.
- General assemblies.
- Parts lists.
- Circuit diagrams for hydraulic, pneumatic, and electrical electronic diagrams using stored standard symbols.

A CAD system requires hardware and software. Hardware is usually the computer, mouse, keyboard, VDU, plotter etc. Software is the programs of instruction which make the hardware operate in the desired manner.

Hardware

Computers for CAD range in size from the very large to the type of computer that can be found in the home, the PC. The very large computers are usually **mainframes** and will normally be based within very large companies or institutions. Those somewhat smaller are referred to as **mini-computers** and the last, but growing in capacity, is the **micro-computer** or PC. Generally computers are identified by their 'word length'. This represents the size or number of bits of data that can be transmitted in parallel e.g. 8 bit, 16 bit, 32 bit. Usually the longer the word length the more complex the CAD system that can be operated. Until a number of years ago micro-computers had 8 bit word length, and mainframe computers had 32 bit word length, but micro computers with 32 bit word length are now commonplace. The speed of development of the computer chip makes writing about them difficult as today what is most up-to-date will tomorrow see a new development announced. In these notes four configurations of computer systems will be identified in very general terms.

- **Centralised system**

  This is usually based on a mainframe computer which is capable of supporting a large number of terminals (30+) operating at the same time. This system has a very large initial cost but has high computing power and extra terminals may be added at a relatively low cost. One drawback is that if a large number of operators are accessing the computer at the same time the response from the computer becomes slow. See Fig. 17.2(a).

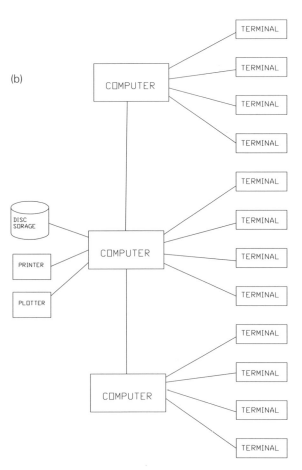

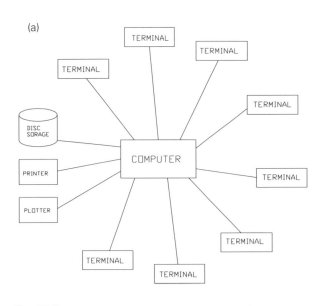

Fig. 17.2

- **Multiple host system**

  An example of this type of system may be seen when two or more mini-computer systems each with a limited number of terminals are linked together. This has the advantage that it would appear to the user that they are connected to a centralised system, and that if one computer should fail then only a limited number of terminals would be affected. See Fig. 17.2(b).

- **Distributed processing**

  This is a system in which each terminal has its own computer. All the computers are connected into a network arrangement to form an integrated system. The computers could be micros, minis, even a mainframe. Today they are usually micros. This system would share the use of such hardware as plotters, printers and storage devices and all software except the operating system for each PC. See Fig. 17.3(a).

- **Stand alone system**

  This is a system in which the user has access to a single computer which is usually dedicated to one type of work. Today these are found in many companies. They have the advantage that they can work independently of any system the company might have and the cost is relatively low. There are some disadvantages, the main one being memory size, but this is gradually being removed as development of the chip races ahead. See Fig. 17.3(b).

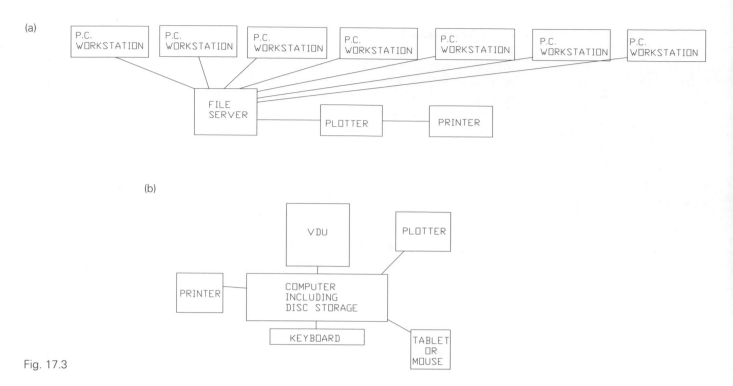

Fig. 17.3

Memory

This is the storage area which holds part of the programme being used as well as the data being generated, the immediate access memory or RAM (random access memory). Ten to fifteen years ago 10 Mbytes of memory was typical on a large computer system but today a micro-computer can have as much as 256 Mbytes and this is expanding.

Storage

Most systems use some form of magnetic disc to store the data generated. This is sometimes referred to as the backing store. A range of systems are available:

- **Non-removable disc**
  This type of system is used a great deal and can have up to 10 gigabytes of space (this is expanding as development never ceases).
- **Removable disc**
  There are two types, the hard disc and the floppy disc. The hard disc can only be found on the mainframe and the mini systems and will store large amounts of data. The floppy discs can be used on all systems and today the most popular size is the 3·5″ disc which will hold 1·44 Mbytes of data.

Up to this point the word terminal has been used to denote the point at which the operator performs the tasks required. There are a number of other terms, but one you may come into contact with frequently particularly when working with micro-computers is **work station**. Whatever type of computer being used there are additional items which are a necessary part of the terminal or workstation. Some of these items are:

- Graphics display unit (VDU, monitor, or simply the screen).
- Keyboard.
- Mouse (joystick, tracker ball etc.).
- Digitising board.
- Graphics tablet.
- Plotter.
- Printer.

All these items require a manual to explain them in clear detail. Therefore these notes should be looked upon only as a reminder after further reading, additional notes and practice.

- **Graphics display unit**

  Other terms used are visual display unit (VDU), monitor or screen. This looks very similar to a television set, the screen being made up of many very small dots. The more dots the better, giving a better picture resolution, but this does make it more expensive. The better or higher, the resolution means that when a line is shown diagonally across the screen it will appear as a straight line rather than a stepped or staircased line.

- **Keyboard**

  There are many variations in use, some quite simple, others with additional features for a specific task. Some are designed to eliminate any physical stress that may occur in the hand, wrists or arm of the operator. Most have one hundred plus keys. These will consist of the functions keys usually denoted by an F number, e.g., F5. In addition to the normal full Qwerty keys there are some additional ones such as Esc, Ctrl and Alt. On many keyboards the keys on the right-hand side are the numeric pad, which also have a dual function. Some of these keys are repeated between the Qwerty keys and the numeric pad, e.g. the cursor keys, page up and page down.

- **Mouse (and other input items)**

  The mouse is a small rectangular object connected to the computer by means of a small cable. Many have two or three buttons allowing inputs of position selection and menu item selection etc. The mouse is very popular with many CAD systems as its cost is relatively small. Alternative input devices are the joystick and tracker ball. The joystick is usually associated with games but some systems use it. The tracker ball has gained popularity with some as the hand can rest on it and does not give too much stress on the arm.

- **Digitising board**

  This looks like a drawing board and comes in a range of sizes. It is an expensive item but some companies have found it very useful in putting existing drawing into the computer. The device allows direct input of data to a computer from a drawing arranged on its surface by means of a cursor. The operator moves the cursor over the surface and registers the coordinates by means of a button.

- **Graphics tablet**

  This is a small low resolution digitising board (Fig. 17.4). It can be used as a digitising board but is more popularly used to input menu commands and as a **free hand** drawing aid. The input of commands requires the tablet to have a preprinted overlay on its surface, usually provided by the software supplier.

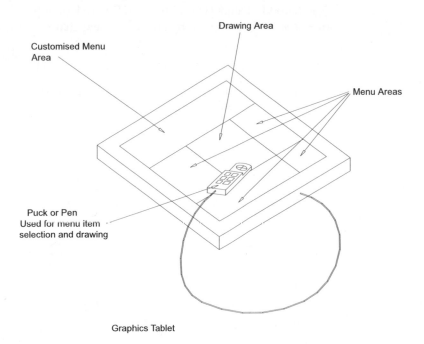

Graphics Tablet

Fig. 17.4

- **Plotter**

This is the means of producing the drawing in hard copy. There are a number of types but the leading ones at this time are the following:

> Drum plotter
> Flatbed plotter
> Electrostatic plotter

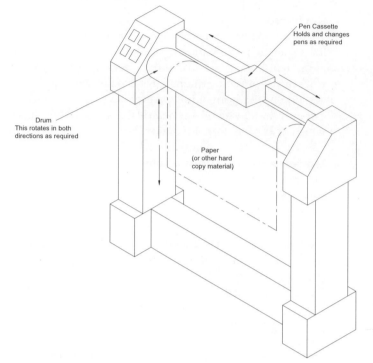

Fig. 17.5

The drum plotter (Fig. 17.5) consists of a drum over which the paper is held. A pen is moved across the drum and held at right angles to its surface. The drum rotating backwards and forwards together with the pen moving across produces lines and all types of curves. Most drum plotters will incorporate some means of automatic pen changing to allow for different colours and line thickness.

The flatbed plotters (Fig. 17.6) are different in that the paper is held flat and does not move. It is held in position by an electrostatic charge or by a vacuum. The pen is held in

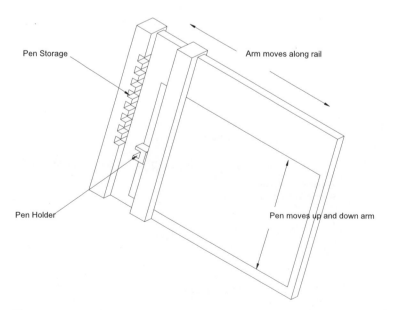

Fig. 17.6

a device which is mounted on a vertical arm and is moved up and down this arm. The arm itself is moved back and forth across the board thus producing lines and all types of curves. Pen can be changed as with the drum type.

The electrostatic plotters are more expensive, but many users have shown a preference towards them as they require less attention once set up. They are similar to laser printers.

- **Printers**

Most users prefer the laser printer as small drawing (up to A3) can be produced on these thus giving a dual function.

Software

There are two basic types of software required to run any computer system:

- System software.
- Application software.

System software

This is the operating system which makes the hardware function effectively. Modern operating systems are made up of a collection of integrated modules which perform such functions as hardware management and peripheral device control, and generate the user interface. This interface allows the user to communicate with the computer; common operating systems are Unix, DOS, C/PM, Windows, etc. You will learn more about this topic as part of your IT training.

Application software

This is the software that makes the hardware into a CAD system. Generally the software will be written in a high-level compiled language such as Fortran or Pascal. A variety of CAD applications are available:

- 2D draughting packages can be obtained in various degrees of sophistication to include a range of drawing facilities. The degree of sophistication is reflected in the cost.
- 3D modelling packages usually require the use of a 32-bit computer and can produce wire frame, surface modelling and solid modelling images.
- Finite element analysis packages are usually for the larger computer but as the micro computer gains in power and packages with limited size have been written their use has been increased. These types of package are used to analyse the mechanical loading characteristics of engineering components.
- Ergonomic analysis packages allow the study of the relationship between the human being and the working environment. The considerations include such areas as workspace, heating and lighting, tools, machines and methods of organisation.
- There are many other applications on the market which each fill a specific need. Typically these are centroids, second moments of area, bearing load calculations, surface development and more specialist packages.

Exercises

Briefly investigate the CAD system you have available. Determine:

1 The type of system.

2 The operating system used.

3 The software used.

4 The links with other software that are possible.

Chapter 18

Drawing exercises

The purpose of this chapter is to give the student the experience of producing engineering drawings in 1st and 3rd angle projection by both traditional and computer-aided methods. The exercises are graded so that the requirements and knowledge needed to complete each task is increased.

1. A drawing in 3rd angle projection is required of the component shown in Fig. 18.1(a). The views should be:
   (a) A front elevation as seen by taking the section on AA.
   (b) A plan.
   (c) An appropriate end elevation.

   The drawing should be completed by the addition of a simplified border layout which should give your name, date started and completed, title, projection used, scale, drawing units, and any college reference required. Do not include dimensions.

2. Produce a drawing in 1st angle projection of the shaft steady shown in Fig. 18.1(b). The views required are:
   (a) A sectional front elevation, the section being taken on AA.
   (b) An end elevation.
   (c) A plan.

   The drawing should be completed by the addition of a simplified layout. This should include your name, date started and completed, title, projection used, scale, drawing units, and any college reference required. Do not include dimensions.

(a)　　　　　　　　　　　　　　　　　　　　　(b)

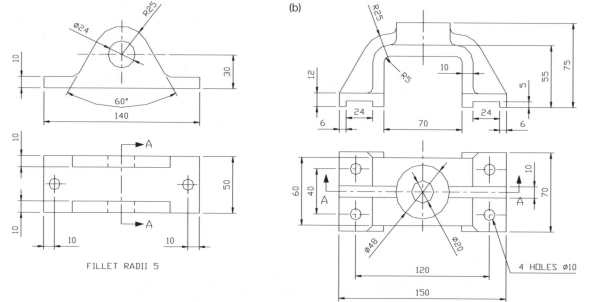

Fig. 18.1

3. Produce a drawing in 3rd angle projection of the forged bracket shown in Fig. 18.2(a). The drawing should have a front elevation, end elevation and a plan; one of the views should be in section. The drawing should give all the information required to produce the bracket, but geometrical tolerances should be omitted.
4. A full working drawing is required of the cast bracket shown in Fig. 18.2(b). It is suggested that there should be two sectional views and that it should be drawn in 1st angle projection. The drawing should give all the information required to produce the bracket.

(a)

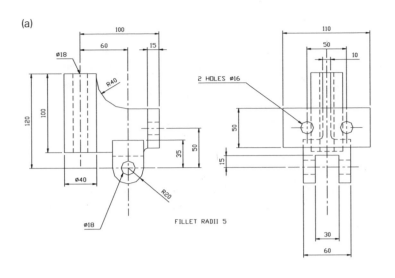

(b)

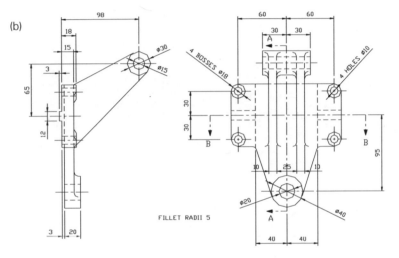

Fig. 18.2

5. A casting for a valve body is shown in Fig. 18.3(a). Produce a working drawing for the valve body with the appropriate sectional view/s. It should be noted that all three flanges are identical. The drawing should be produced in an appropriate scale and projection.

6. Figure 18.3(b) shows a forged lever. Produce a full working drawing in 3rd angle projection with appropriate sections. The lever is to have two bushes inserted in the counter bored holes of 20 mm dia. and 30 mm dia. (Note the bush for the larger hole is to be a split bush.) The bushes are to be made of a bearing material and their fit into the forging is to be a close clearance. Choose and apply the appropriate tolerances.

7. Produce a full working drawing of the cast mounting bracket shown in Fig. 18.4(a). The drawing should be in 1st angle projection with all the information necessary for manufacture. The drawing should also include an additional view to show the true shape and position of the bosses.

8. A full working drawing of the cast lever shown in Fig. 18.4(b) is required in 3rd angle projection. The lever is to be mounted on a shaft by the 30 mm dia. hole. The fit of this shaft in the hole is close clearance.

(a)

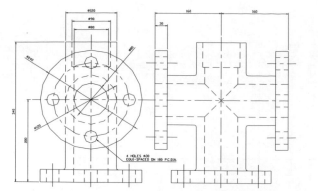

(b)

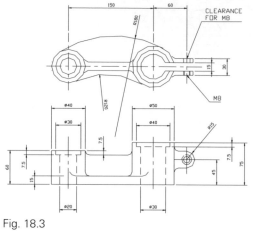

CLEARANCE
FOR M8

M8

Fig. 18.3

(a)

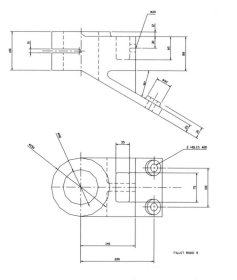

FILLET RADII 5

(b)

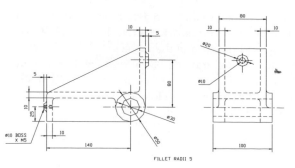

FILLET RADII 5

Fig. 18.4

Chapter 19

Assessment

The purpose of this chapter is to provide the student with the assessments required to ensure that all the performance criteria across the range required can be met for each of the elements given in the **BTEC Additional Unit 37: Engineering Drawing (Advanced)**. This is done by providing:

- A study plan.
- An assessment plan.
- Assignments covering each of the elements in the unit.
- Guidance for the grading of the assignments.
- Details of the performance criteria and core skills covered in each assignment.

Study plan

The plan as set out in Table 19.1 has been designed assuming that the unit is to be studied for half the academic year (18 weeks) during the 1st year of the Advanced Programme. The teaching time may be one or two periods per week, but it is emphasised that the student is expected to complete a substantial amount of work during his/her own time.

Table 19.1   Study plan

Period no.	Topic area	Additional work to be undertaken by student
1	The activities of the drawing office Intro. to traditional DO equipment The drawing sheet	Use library to further introduce activities of DO, the use of the drawing sheet and its material
2 & 3	Basic geometrical constructions	Complete exercises
4	Advanced geometrical constructions	Complete exericses
5	Intro. to orthographic projection	Additional work on basic projection
6	Development	Complete development exercises
	Assignment No. 1	*To be attempted when student is ready*
7	Introduction to British Standards Types of engineering drawing	Closer look at BS 308 and other BS Review how types of drawing are used
8	Further work on orthographic projection	Complete projection exercises
9	Pictorial views	Isometric and oblique projection exercises
10	Sectioning	Complete sectioning exercises
11 & 12	Dimensioning, tolerancing and geometrical tolerancing	Complete all tolerancing exercises and additional ones if required

(*continued*)

Table 19.1 (*continued*)

Period no.	Topic area	Additional work to be undertaken by student
	Assignment No. 2	*To be attempted when student is ready*
13	Circuit diagrams	Use CAD to build library and apply
	Assignment No. 3	*To be attempted when student is ready*
14	Auxiliary views	Complete graded exercises
15 & 16	CAD/CAM	Additional reading and complete exercises
17 & 18	Engineering drawing Traditional and computer-aided methods	Use traditional and CAD methods to produce drawings for the portfolio Produce additional drawing if required
	Assignment No. 4	*To be attempted when student is ready*

This plan is only a guide. It is anticipated that some students, particularly those with previous engineering or technical drawing experience, will complete the various topic areas ahead of the time given thus allowing the students to give time to other unit areas.

It is expected that by allowing students to progress at their own pace they will be at varying stages of the learning process during the period of study. Therefore assessment will be determined by the student in consultation with the lecturer.

When all assignments have been successfully completed the performance criteria across the range stated in the unit should have been achieved.

When completing the examples, graded exercises and assignments it is recommended that both traditional and computer-aided methods be used. Most students, given a free hand, will perform the geometrical constructions by traditional means and the component and assembly drawings by CAD. It is suggested that some geometrical constructions be attempted using CAD and at least one component drawing be attempted using traditional methods. This will assist the student in making a valid comparison between both methods. Although this is not a requirement of the unit it will provide the knowledge and understanding for Core Skills Information Technology Unit 3.4.3 and assist with the Additional Unit 30: Computer-Aided Design/Computer-Aided Manufacture (CAD/CAM) Advanced.

Assessment plan

Table 19.2   Assessment plan

Assignment no.	Question no.	Topic area	Unit/element/PC ref.	Max. mark
1	1	The role of the drawing office	–	5
	2–4	Basic geometrical constrictions	–	32
	5–8	Advanced geometrical constrictions	37.1.1, 37.1.2 37.1.3, 37.1.4	43
			Assign. Total	**80**

(*continued*)

Table 19.2   (*continued*)

Assignment no.	Question no.	Topic area	Unit/element/PC ref.	Max. mark
2	1	Component drawing	37.2.3	20
	2	Dimensions and tolerances	37.2.2	15
	3	Assembly drawing	37.2.1	15
	4	Pictorial drawing	37.2.4	10
			Assign. Total	**60**
3	1	Circuit diagram – electrical etc.	37.3.2, 37.3.4	25
		Circuit diagram – pneumatic etc.	37.3.1, 37.3.3	25
			Assign. Total	**50**
4	1	Component and assembly drawing	37.2.1, 37.2.3	**60**
			Total	**250**

It is recommended that all assignments be presented with a standard front sheet and additional sheets allowing for student planning and lecturer feedback. Examples are given on the next pages.

In addition to providing the means to enable the student to obtain the skills, knowledge and understanding and present these as evidence of achievement the work also contributes to a number of other units. Students should also note that in the Contents or Index of the portfolio at least two references for all performance criteria within the range specified must be made.

Other units for which a contribution could be claimed:

- **Mandatory Unit No. 5 Design Development (Advanced)**
  Element 3 – Using technical drawing to communicate design for engineering products and engineering services.
  Performance criteria   1 – Chapters 9 and 10
  3 – Chapters 9, 10, 11, 15, 16 and 18
  4 – Chapter 18
- **Core Skills Unit – Application of Number (Level 3)**
  Element 1 – Collect and record data
  Performance criteria 4 – Chapters 12 and 13
  Element 3 – Interpret and record data
  Performance criteria 2 – Chapters 13 and 14
- **Core Skills Unit – Communication (Level 3)**
  Element 3 – Use images
  Performance criteria   1 – Chapters 9 and 10
  2 – Chapters 9 and 10
  3 – Chapters 9 and 10
  Element 4 – Read and respond to written material
  Performance criteria – all – Chapter 17 and the exercises
- **Core Skills Unit – Information Technology (Level 3)**
  Element 1 – Prepare information
  Performance criteria   2 – All CAD operations
  5 – CAD operations
  Element 2 – Process information
  Performance criteria 2 – CAD operations
  Element 3 – Present information
  Performance criteria   3 – All CAD operations
  4 – Plotting out of drawings produced in CAD
  5 – Full engineering drawings produced in CAD

ASSIGNMENT/ACTIVITY SHEET

Student's name: _____

Course title: **GNVQ Advanced – Engineering**

Assignment/activity title: _____

Lecturer: _____   *Assessor:* _____

Date issued		*Date for completion*		*Date received*	

Elements/performance criteria covered: _____

_____

_____

Core skills covered: _____

_____

Grade awarded

Assessor's signature

Theme	Criteria	Pass	Merit	Distinction
Planning	**1** Drawing up plans of action			
	2 Monitoring courses of action			
Information seeking and handling	**3** Identifying and using sources to obtain information			
	4 Establishing the validity of information			
Evaluation	**5** Evaluating outcomes and activities			
	6 Justifying particular approaches to tasks			
Quality of outcomes	**7** Synthesis			
	8 Command of language			

Assessor's general comments

ASSIGNMENT/ACTIVITY REVIEW AND FEEDBACK

Feedback after completion of assignment/activity

Grading feedback

Action reqired for improvement of future assignment/activities

Student's signature and date

Assessor's signature and date

ASSIGNMENT ACTIVITY ACTION PLAN

Assignment title:

Theme:

Student name:

Tutor:

Date commenced/completed:

What do I need to find out?	What do I need to do?	In which order?	By when?	Has it been achieved?	If not, why not?	What do I do next?

REVIEWS

Next review date	Tutor's signature	Student's signature

Tutor comments		

Engineering drawing assignment 1

Introduction

The objectives of this assignment are to assess your knowledge of the drawing office, geometrical construction techniques and development using traditional drawing methods.

Reference may be made to notes and work previously completed but assistance from any other source may affect the grade awarded.

Task

To compile notes and a portfolio of drawings which will include the following:

- Notes on the activities of the drawing office.
- Geometrical constructions.
- Tangents.
- Loci.
- Cams.
- Development.

Each of the tasks is designed to ensure that, if completed successfully, some of the performance criteria across the range required by the unit will be achieved.

All tasks should be produced on A3 paper pre-prepared with a border and small title block indicating:

- Name of student.
- Date started and completed.
- Unit number.
- Questions attempted.

Resources available

The conventional drawing equipment available in the drawing room, the student's own drawing instruments and previously completed drawings and notes.

Grading and assessment criteria

- **Pass (P)**
  All tasks completed to a satisfactory standard. Some help was required to determine the methods used to complete the constructions (but not step-by-step instruction) for a maximum of four questions. Drawing standards were acceptable.
- **Merit (M)**
  All tasks completed to a significantly better than satisfactory standard. Some help was required, e.g. the method to be used to complete, but not to start up, a maximum of two questions. Drawing standards were good but fell short of BS 308.
- **Distinction (D)**
  All questions completed to a high standard. No help was given to complete any part of the task. The standard of drawing was to BS 308.

Exercises

1. Make brief notes on the following:
   (a) The role of the standards section.
   (b) Three disadvantages of drawing office computerisation.
2. Produce the following constructions:
   (a) A horizontal line, 70 mm long, divided into the ratio 1:3:2.

(b) A right angle using only a straight edge and dividers. Then produce 60° and 22·5° angles on this right angle.

(c) A hexagon 50 mm A/F using any method.

3. Draw two circles on a horizontal centre line with the distance between centres of 70 mm. The left-hand circle to have a diameter of 50 mm and the right-hand to have a diameter of 30 mm. Construct a tangent to both circles, the tangent being at the top of the circles.

4. Reproduce the shape shown in Fig. 19.1 accurately. All construction lines to be shown.

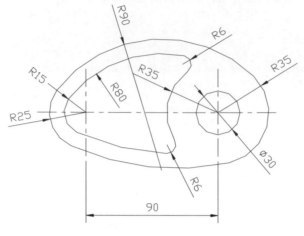

Fig. 19.1

5. Reproduce the mechanism shown in Fig. 19.2 and plot the loci of point P and Q. A rotates about O, C is a fixed pivot with the rod PQ sliding through.

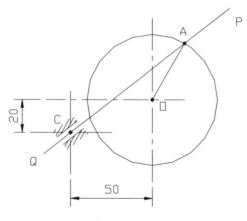

OA = 40, AP = 35, AQ = 110

Fig. 19.2

6. Produce a cam with the following details:
   - Plate cam.
   - Clockwise rotation.
   - 20 mm dia roller follower, in line.
   - 30 mm dia cam shaft.
   - Least radius of cam 35 mm.
   - 0–180° rise of 64 mm with simple harmonic motion.
   - 180–240° dwell.
   - 240–360° fall 64 mm with constant velocity.

7. Construct three turns of a helix with a cylinder diameter of 75 mm and a lead of 30 mm.

8. Copy the elevation of the intersection of two pipes shown in Fig. 19.3. Construct the curve of intersection and draw the developed shape of part B.

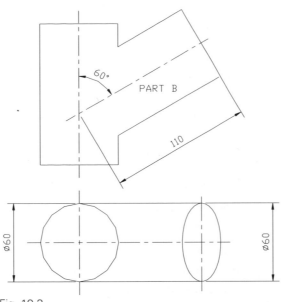

Fig. 19.3

The suggested mark allocation is given in Table 20.1.

Table 20.1   Suggested mark allocation

Question no.	Requirements	Possible mark	Actual mark
1	Role correctly described	2	
	Three disadvantages correctly given	3	
2(a)	Line drawn accurately	2	
	Number of divisions and ratio obtained correctly	2	
	Line quality	2	
2(b)	Right angle constructed accurately	2	
	60° angle constructed and accurate	2	
	22·5° angle constructed and accurate	2	
	Line quality	2	
2(c)	Hexagon accurate using appropriate method	2	
	Line quality	2	
3	Figure constructed accurately	2	
	Tangent constructed correctly	2	
	Line quality	2	
4	Figure accurately reproduced	2	
	All construction methods appropriate	4	
	Line quality	2	
5	Figure accurately drawn	2	
	Plotting of point P and Q accurate	2	
	Standard of curve drawing	2	
	Line quality	2	

(continued)

Table 20.1 (*continued*)

Question no.	Requirements	Possible mark	Actual mark
6	Clockwise rotation	2	
	Roller dia	2	
	Least radius 35 mm	2	
	Rise 64 mm	2	
	SHM construction	4	
	Dwell	2	
	Fall 64 mm	2	
	Constant velocity construction	2	
	Line quality	2	
7	Dia, lead and no. Turn correct	2	
	Plotting accurate	2	
	Curve drawn accurately	3	
8	Elevation drawn correctly and accurate	2	
	Curve of intersection drawn correctly and accurate	3	
	Development of part B correct and accurate	3	
	Total	**80**	
	Grade awarded		

Engineering drawing assignment 2

Introduction

The objectives of this assignment are to assess your knowledge and application of the techniques required to produce engineering drawings, tolerances and pictorial views by either traditional or computer-aided techniques. Reference may be made to notes and work previously completed but assistance from any other source may affect the grade awarded.

Task

To produce drawings for inclusion in a portfolio. These drawings to include:

- A component drawing in orthographic projection.
- The application of tolerances to an engineering component.
- An assembly drawing with all references.
- A pictorial view of an engineering component.

Each of the tasks is designed to ensure that, if completed successfully, some of the performance criteria across the range required by the unit will be achieved.

All tasks should be produced on A3 paper. For the application of tolerances and the pictorial drawing the sheet should have a pre-prepared border and small title block indicating:

- Name of student.
- Date started and completed.
- Unit number.
- Questions attempted on that sheet.

Resources available

Traditional and computer-aided drawing equipment, student's own previously prepared notes and drawings.

Grading and assessment criteria

- **Pass (P)**
  All tasks completed to a satisfactory standard. Help was required to determine the method necessary to complete question number 1 and to check the assembly in question number 3 (but not step-by-step instruction). Drawing standards were acceptable.
- **Merit (M)**
  All tasks completed to a significantly better than satisfactory standard. Some help was required, e.g. advice on the requirements on the completion, but not to start up, a maximum of two questions. Drawing standards were good but fell short of BS 308.
- **Distinction (D)**
  All tasks completed to a high standard. No help was given to complete any part of the task. The standard of drawing was to BS 308.

Exercises

1. Produce a drawing to be used in the manufacture of the component shown in Fig. 19.4. This may be produced by traditional or computer-aided techniques.

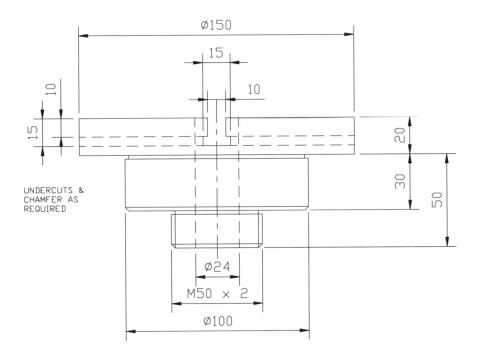

Fig. 19.4

2. Add to the drawing shown in Fig. 19.5 dimensions, tolerances, and geometrical tolerances that are required to produce the component so that it may be manufactured effectively and will function efficiently.
3. Figure 19.6 shows the individual components that make up a small hand vice. Produce an assembly drawing with the jaws open 30 mm.
4. Make an isometric drawing of the component shown in Fig. 19.7. Isometric scale need not be used.

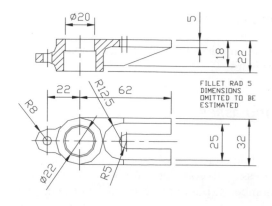

Fig. 19.5

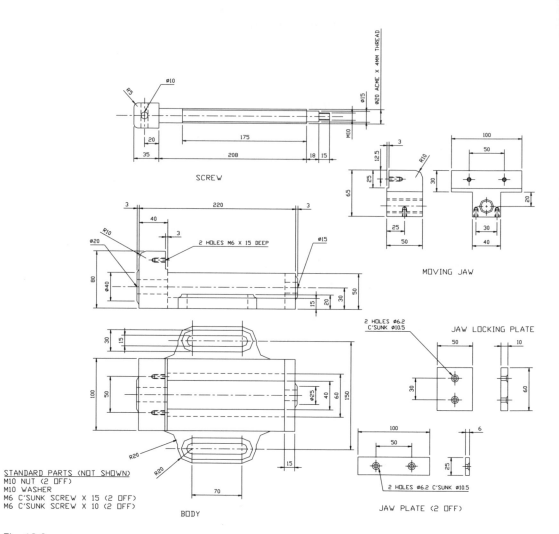

Fig. 19.6

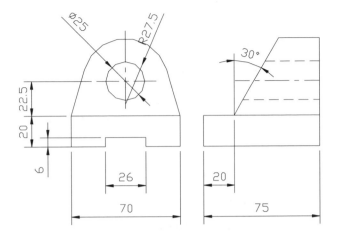

Fig. 19.7

The suggested mark allocation is given in Table 20.2.

Table 20.2   Suggested mark allocation

Question no.	Requirements	Possible mark	Actual mark
1	Drawing sheet with border prepared correctly to include:		
	Material, any treatment and finish	2	
	Dates, issue and signatures	2	
	Units used, overall tolerances	2	
	Title and drawing number	2	
	Other points include – projection stated and correct	2	
	All dimensions given	4	
	Section correctly taken and called up	2	
	Line quality satisfactory	2	
	Overall appearance	2	
	Sub total	**20**	
2	Dimensions applied correctly	2	
	Tolerances applied correctly	4	
	Tolerances mathematically correct	3	
	Geometric tolerances applied satisfactorily	6	
	Sub total	**15**	
3	Drawing sheet prepared as required	1	
	Assembled correctly	2	
	Projection stated and correct	1	
	All items referenced	2	
	Parts list included and correct	3	
	Jaws open correct distance	2	
	Line quality satisfactory	2	
	Overall appearance	2	
	Sub total	**15**	

(*continued*)

Table 20.2   (continued)

Question no.	Requirements	Possible mark	Actual mark
4	Drawing sheet prepared as required	1	
	Isometric axis correct	1	
	Component correct shape in all faces	3	
	Line quality satisfactory	2	
	Overall appearance	3	
	Sub total	**10**	
	Total	**60**	
	Grade awarded		

Engineering drawing assignment 3

Introduction

The objectives of this assignment are to assess the student's knowledge and application of the symbols used to represent pneumatic, hydraulic, electrical and electronic components in circuit diagrams. Reference may be made to notes and work previously completed but assistance from any other source may affect the grade awarded.

Task

To produce circuit diagrams for pneumatic/hydraulic and electrical/electronic systems. The task is designed to ensure that, if completed successfully, some of the performance criteria across the range required by the unit will be achieved.

The task should be completed on A3 paper with a pre-prepared border and small title block indicating:

- Name of student
- Date started and completed
- Unit number
- Number of question attempted

Resources available

Traditional and computer-aided equipment, student's own previously prepared notes and drawings together with the relevant British Standard symbols.

Grading and assessment criteria

- **Pass (P)**
  Task completed to a satisfactory standard. Help was required to determine the methods used to construct the symbols (but not step-by-step instruction). Drawing standards were acceptable and symbols conformed to British Standards.
- **Merit (M)**
  Task completed to a significantly better than satisfactory standard. Some help was required, e.g. advice on the completion, but not to start up, of a maximum of one question. Drawing standards were good but fell short of BS 308 and symbols conformed to British Standards.
- **Distinction (D)**
  Task completed to a high standard. No help was given in completing the task. The standard of drawing was to BS 308 and symbols conformed to British Standards.

Exercises

1. Produce a circuit diagram for a pneumatic circuit using traditional means. It is suggested that the circuit selected should be of a machine tool used in the engineering workshop with which the student is familiar.
2. Produce a circuit diagram for an electrical/electronic circuit using computer-aided means. It is suggested that the circuit should be one that the student has become familiar with when studying the Mandatory Unit Science for Engineers.

The suggested mark allocation is given in Table 20.3.

Table 20.3   Suggested mark allocation

Task no.	Requirements	Possible mark	Actual mark
1	Line work of symbols	5	
	Symbols to British Standards	10	
	Circuit drawn correctly	5	
	Layout is readable	5	
	Full presentation	5	
	Sub total	**30**	
2	Line work of symbols	5	
	Symbols to British Standards	10	
	Circuit drawn correctly	5	
	Layout is readable	5	
	Full presentation	5	
	Sub total	**30**	
	Total	**60**	
	Grade awarded		

Engineering drawing assignment 4

The objectives of this assignment are to assess the student's knowledge and application of engineering drawing.

Task

To produce full working drawings and an assembly drawing from a basic design outline. The task is designed to ensure that, if completed successfully, some of the performance criteria across the range required by the unit will be achieved.

The task should be answered on the correct drawing sheet with all details necessary for manufacture.

Resources available

Traditional and computer-aided equipment, student's own previously completed notes and drawings.

Grading and assessment criteria

- **Pass (P)**
  The task was completed to a satisfactory standard. Help was required to determine an outline of the plan of action to attempt the task (but not step-by-step instruction) and general advice on dimensioning. Drawing standards were acceptable.

- **Merit (M)**

  The task was completed to a significantly better than satisfactory standard. Some help was required, e.g. deciding what additional views are required for a maximum of one item. Drawing standards were good but fell short of BS 308.

- **Distinction (D)**

  All questions completed to a high standard. No help was given to complete any part of the task. The standard of drawing was to BS 308.

Exercises

An experimental oil burner is shown in Fig. 19.8.

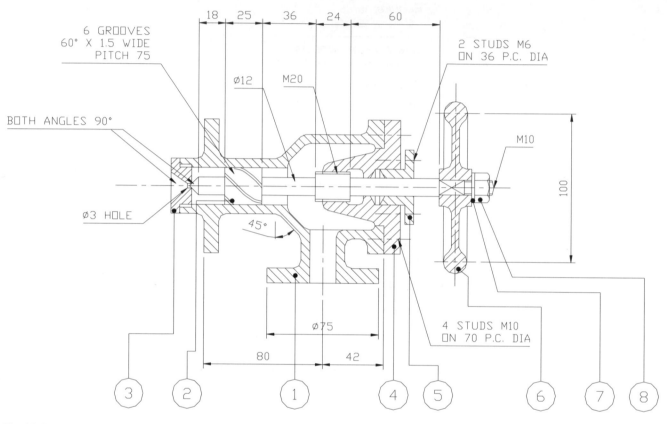

Fig. 19.8

1. Produce working drawings for each of the components.
2. Produce an assembly drawing.

The suggested mark allocation is given in Table 20.4.

Table 20.4   Suggested mark allocation

Item no.	Requirements	Possible mark	Actual mark
All sheets	Correctly prepared drawing sheet to include:	2	
	Material, any treatment and finish	2	
	Dates, issue and signatures	2	
	Units used, overall tolerances	2	
	Title and drawing number	2	
	Projection stated and correct	2	
	Overall dimension tolerances	2	

(continued)

Table 20.4 (*continued*)

Item no.	Requirements	Possible mark	Actual mark
1	Dimensions and tolerances applied correctly	4	
	Geometric tolerances applied satisfactorily	4	
	Views and sections chosen correctly	2	
	Drawing standard	2	
2	Dimensions and tolerances applied correctly	4	
	Geometric tolerances applied satisfactorily	4	
	Views and sections chosen correctly	2	
	Drawing standard	2	
	Additional views added	2	
3	Dimensions and tolerances applied correctly	4	
	Geometric tolerances applied satisfactorily	4	
	Views and sections chosen correctly	2	
	Drawing standard	2	
4	Dimensions and tolerances applied correctly	4	
	Geometric tolerances applied satisfactorily	4	
	Views and sections chosen correctly	2	
	Drawing standard	2	
5	Dimensions and tolerances applied correctly	4	
	Geometric tolerances applied satisfactorily	4	
	Views and sections chosen correctly	2	
	Drawing standard	2	
6	Dimensions and tolerances applied correctly	4	
	Geometric tolerances applied satisfactorily	4	
	Views and sections chosen correctly	2	
	Drawing standard	2	
Assy	Views and sections chosen correctly	4	
	References correct	2	
	Parts list correct	4	
	Drawing standards	2	
	Total	**100**	
	Grade awarded		

Chapter 20

Glossary of terms

This Glossary covers many terms you may find being used in computer-aided engineering as well as those used in this workbook.

ASCII
American Standard Code for Information Interchange: a definition of the precise format in which data is sent and received between systems and devices.

Application software
Software written to solve a set of unique tasks, e.g. computer-aided design and draughting.

Bit
Binary digit: the smallest unit of data storage in a computer.

Byte
A collection of eight data bits used to represent a character or a number.

CAD (or CADD)
Computer-aided draughting (or computer-aided design and draughting): the application of a computer to aid the design process and the production of drawings.

CAD/CAM
Computer-aided design/computer-aided manufacture: the application of a computer system to aid the design and manufacture of any product.

CAE
Computer-aided engineering: the automating, by the use of a computer, of all steps involved in the manufacturing of a product from concept to marketing.

CAM
Computer-aided manufacturing: the application of a computer to aid the manufacturing processes.

CAPM
Computer-aided production management: a system to control the production and material requirements of the manufacturing process.

Cartesian co-ordinates
A means of expressing the position of a point with reference to axes set at right angles to one another.

CIM
Computer integrated manufacture: the total approach to automating, using a computer, all processes required to manufacture a product.

CNC
Computer numerical control: using a computer linked to a machine tool to control the cutting tool path.

CPU
Central processing unit: the central element of a computer. It includes memory, the arithmetic logic unit and the control unit.

Command

An instruction to a computer system to perform an operation, the instruction being input by means of one of the interactive devices, i.e. keyboard, mouse etc.

Co-ordinate system

A two-dimensional system used to place a point or geometry on a drawing.

Cursor

A symbol, which appears on the monitor screen, and moves under the control of a pointing device, such as a mouse, pen or puck.

Data

Information in a form which can be used and stored in a computer.

Database

Information stored in a central place that can be accessed by many applications programs.

DBMS

Database management system: software for the efficient creation, storage and retrieval of information in a way which suits the application and the user.

Deviation

The difference between the basic size and the maximum or minimum permissible size of a dimension.

Digitiser

A large electronic board, which may look similar to a drawing board, from which positional data or commands may be selected using a puck or stylus pen. This allows an existing conventional drawing to be **traced** into the computer.

Disk

A mass storage device consisting of a flat, round sheet coated with ferrous oxide. The disk, in operation, rotates at high speed thus giving fast access time.

Display (or Monitor/VDU)

The computer device that is similar to a television set (VDU: visual display unit).

Dragging

The moving of selected parts on a display across the screen under the direction of an interactive device, i.e. mouse, pen etc.

Drum plotter

A device for producing drawings on paper or other media. The paper moves in one direction giving one axis and the pen/s move at right angles to this movement. The combination of these two movements enables all shapes to be drawn including circles.

FEA

Finite element analysis: a technique used to define a component by breaking it down into many parts. Each of these parts (or elements) can have simulated forces applied to it and by calculating the movement of each element for a given force applied the overall movement of the component can be determined. This method can be used for other engineering analysis.

File

A set of data stored in a computer or on a disk under a given name.

Flat bed plotter

A device for producing drawings on paper or other media. The paper is fixed to the flat surface usually by electrostatic means. Pens are housed in a rack from which they can be automatically selected by the pen holder. The pen holder is part of an arm which bridges the flat drawing area. This arm is moved over the drawing area and the pen holder can be moved up and down the arm. These combined movements allow any shape to be drawn.

Floppy disk

A circular disk that can be magnetised to hold computer information.

Function key

A key used to execute a command, call up a standard symbol etc. The key may be marked on the keyboard as F1 to F12 but any key can be defined as a function key.

Grade

An indication of the size of the tolerance for a given dimension. The lower the grade the finer or smaller the tolerance.

Graphics tablet

A small low-resolution (not so accurate) digitising board. These are often used together with an overlay on its surface to aid the selection of commands etc.

Grid

A set of points displayed on the screen, with vertical and horizontally defined pitch, to aid the production of a drawing. The grid will not be stored or plotted out with the drawing.

Hard copy

A printout from a computer system. This may be in the form of text, numeric data or graphics.

Hardware

The electro-mechanical elements that make up a computer system, i.e. screen, keyboard, processor etc.

IGES

Initial Graphic Exchange Standard: a standard format which allows the transfer of a drawing file from one CAD system to another CAD system or a CAM system.

Integrated circuits

A large number of solid state electronic circuits on a slice of silicon. Many contain hundreds of thousands of circuits.

Interfacing

Hardware and/or software that allows two or more systems to link up or integrate.

Joystick

Used to control the cursor movements on a graphics display.

Kilobyte

A unit of memory size. About 1000 Bytes, the exact size being 1024.

LAN

Local area network: computers linked together to enable the transfer of data at high speed.

Layers
May be seen as totally transparent sheets of paper. Each layer can be seen on its own or in conjunction with other specific layers. Each layer is usually reserved for specific purpose, i.e. geometry, construction lines, hidden detail, hatching, etc., and is given a unique reference.

Limits of size
The maximum and minimum permissible size for a dimension that is acceptable.

Load
To put a computer program into the memory of a computer from an external device.

Memory (or main store)
The part of the computer where data and programs are stored when in use.

Menu
A file of commands, instructions and sub-routines which can be accessed by a mouse, keyboard etc.

Megabyte (MB)
A unit of memory size. Approximately 1 million bytes, or 1024 kilobytes to be exact.

Mirror
A command that makes a mirror image copy of selected geometry.

MMC
Maximum material condition: for a shaft this will be the largest permissible size and for a hole this will be the smallest permissible size.

Modem
The is the acronym for modulator/demodulator: a hardware device used to connect a computer system to another computer system by the telephone line.

Mouse
A device for positioning and moving the cursor on the screen. The movement of the mouse sends X and Y co-ordinates to the computer.

Nominal size
The size by which a feature on a component is referred to (i.e. 25 mm , 50 mm).

Operating system
The main suite of programs which control the running of the units of a computer system and provide the link between the computer and the operator. The operating system (OS) looks after such items as the transfer of data around the system, allocation of disk storage etc.

Output device
An electronic or mechanical/electronic device which converts data from a computer into printed or display characters, e.g. monitor, printer.

Pan
A command which moves the screen over the drawing area without altering the size of the window.

Parametric symbol
A symbol used to create a component which has been created with one of more variable dimensions and whose value can be dictated by the user. This allows the quick and accurate construction of a family of parts.

Pixel
The smallest picture element of a graphics display.

Post-processor
A software routine which converts data for output to another activity. Examples are the converting of graphical data for use by the machine tool, converting FEA data into a form that is suitable for a graphics package.

Puck
An input device used on the surface of a graphics table or digitiser. Pucks usually have a set of function buttons incorporated into them.

Qwerty
Used to describe a conventional keyboard. The name being taken from the letters at the top left-hand side of the keyboard.

RAM
Random access memory: the main very fast access storage unit of a computer system. Information will be lost from this area when the computer is switched off. This memory is said to be volatile.

Resolution
The degree of detail that can be obtained on the graphics in a computer system.

ROM
Read only memory: memory which stores information but which cannot be over-written. It is not lost when the computer is switched off. This memory is said to be non-volatile.

Software
All programs used on a computer system.

Tolerance
The difference in the maximum and minimum permissible sizes

Window
A method of selecting an area of a drawing on the graphics screen for enlargement or any other purpose.

Workstation
The CAD/CAM operator's environment. This usually comprises a graphics terminal, input devices, a processor etc.

Zoom
The method of enlarging an area of a drawing displayed on the graphics screen.

Index